THE COSMIC CALCULATOR

A VEDIC MATHEMATICS COURSE FOR SCHOOLS

BOOK 2

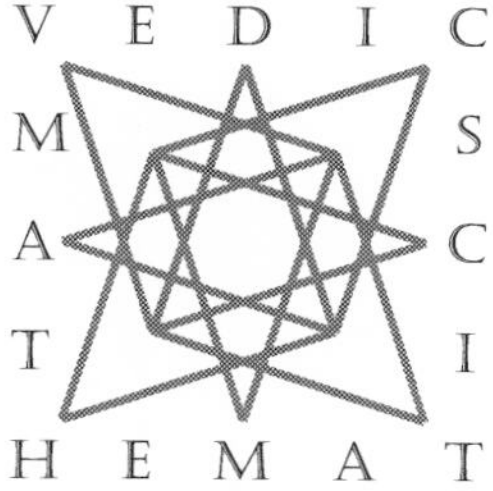

KENNETH WILLIAMS
MARK GASKELL

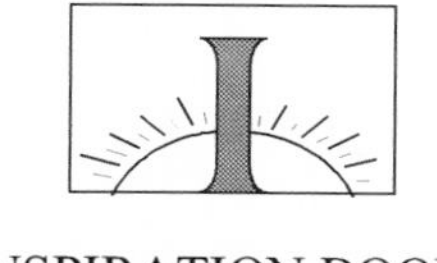

INSPIRATION BOOKS

Published by Inspiration Books, 2010,
Kensglen, Nr Carsphairn, Castle Douglas, DG7 3TE, Scotland, U.K.

Revised Edition 2010
ISBN 978-1-902517-25-4

http://www.vedicmaths.org

Illustrations by David Williams
Cartoons by John Fuller

Front cover painting by Lawrence Sheaff
Floor of Heaven'. Acrylic on board

CONTENTS

VEDIC MATHEMATICS SUTRAS

1	एकाधिकेन पूर्वेण Ekādhikena Pūrveṇa	*By One More than the One Before*
2	निखिलं नवतश्चरमं दशतः Nikhilaṃ Navatascaramaṃ Dasataḥ	*All from 9 and the Last from 10*
3	ऊर्ध्वतिर्यग्भ्याम् Ūrdhva Tiryagbhyāṃ	*Vertically and Crosswise*
4	परावर्त्य योजयेत् Parāvartya Yojayet	*Transpose and Apply*
5	शून्यं साम्यसमुच्चये Sūnyaṃ Sāmyasamuccaya	*If the Samuccaya is the Same it is Zero*
6	आनुरूप्ये शून्यं अन्यत् (Ānurūpya) Sūnyamanyat	*If One is in Ratio the Other is Zero*
7	संकलन व्यवकलनाभ्याम् Saṅkalana Vyavakalanābhyām	*By Addition and by Subtraction*
8	पूरणापूरणाभ्याम् Pūraṇāpūraṇābhyām	*By the Completion or Non-Completion*
9	चलनकलनाभ्याम् Calana Kalanābhyām	*Differential Calculus*
10	यावदूनम् Yāvadūnam	*By the Deficiency*
11	व्यष्टिसमष्टिः Vyaṣṭisamaṣṭiḥ	*Specific and General*
12	शेषाण्यङ्केन चरमेण Seṣaṇyaṅkena Carameṇa	*The Remainders by the Last Digit*
13	सोपान्त्यद्वयमन्त्यं Sopāntyadvayamantyam	*The Ultimate and Twice the Penultimate*
14	एकन्यूनेन पूर्वेण Ekanūnena Pūrveṇa	*By One Less than the One Before*
15	गुणितसमुच्चयः Guṇitsamuccayaḥ	*The Product of the Sum*
16	गुणकसमुच्चयः Guṇakasamuccayaḥ	*All the Multipliers*

SUB-SUTRAS

1	आनुरूप्येण Ānurūpyeṇa	*Proportionately*
2	शिष्यते शेषसंज्ञः Siṣyate Seṣaṃjñaḥ	*The Remainder Remains Constant*
3	आद्यमाद्येनान्त्यमन्त्येन Ādyamādyenāntyamantyena	*The First by the First and the Last by the Last*
4	केवलैः सप्तकं गुण्यात् Kevalaiḥ Saptakaṃ Guṇyāt	*For 7 the Multiplicand is 143*
5	वेष्टनम् Veṣṭanaṃ	*Osculation*
6	यावदूनं तावदूनं Yāvadūnaṃ Tāvadūnaṃ	*Lessen by the Deficiency*
7	यावदूनं तावदूनीकृत्य वर्गं च योजयेत् Yāvadūnaṃ Tāvadūnīkṛtya Vargañca Yojayet	*Whatever the Deficiency lessen by that amount and set up the Square of the Deficiency*
8	अन्त्ययोर्दशकेऽपि Antyayordasake'pi	*Last Totalling 10*
9	अन्त्ययोरेव Antyayoreva	*Only the Last Terms*
10	समुच्चयगुणितः Samuccayagunitaḥ	*The Sum of the Products*
11	लोपनस्थापनाभ्याम् Lopanasthāpanābhyām	*By Alternate Elimination and Retention*
12	विलोकनम् Vilokanam	*By Mere Observation*
13	गुणितसमुच्चयः समुच्चयगुणितः Guṇitsamuccayaḥ Samuccayaguṇitaḥ	*The Product of the Sum is the Sum of the Products*
14	ध्वजाङ्कः Dhvajāṅkaḥ	*On the Flag*

> *"Every move of every ant and elephant, the stars and galaxies, at every moment are in perfect precision in space and time, managed by Vedic Mathematics—the mathematics of pure knowledge."*
>
> Maharishi Mahesh Yogi

INTRODUCTION

Mathematics has three main branches: Arithmetic, Algebra and Geometry.

Arithmetic deals with numbers, of which there are many types. Numbers have various properties and can be combined in various ways.
Algebra deals with symbols, often the letters of the alphabet. These also have their own special properties and can be combined.
Geometry deals with shapes and forms: points, lines, surfaces and solids. There are many different kinds of form and they have many interesting properties.

These three branches develop in a structured way and cover all areas of Mathematics. Some topics in mathematics combine two or three of these branches.

At the beginning of this book you will see a list of Sutras (or formulae) and a list of Sub-Sutras (sub-formulae) which will be a great help in your mathematics work. The word "Sutra" means "thread", and we will find that these formulae link up many areas of mathematics. In fact they describe the way your mind works: they tell you how to go about answering questions. You will be introduced to these Sutras one by one and you will find they are *written in italics* in the book.

You will find that the methods of Vedic Mathematics are very easy and straightforward. So simple, in fact, that you may want to do most of the calculations in your head, mentally. You are encouraged to do this because the Vedic system is a system of mental mathematics. But you should also enjoy the mathematics so you should not struggle to do everything in your head. Except for the mental tests at the beginning of the lesson you are free to use pencil and paper if you like. Have fun!

❋ Please also note the following:

Important facts or laws are contained in a rectangular white box like this one. This will help you to refer back to them and to revise your work.

There is an answer book which has answers to the exercises.

Where you see a star like the one at the top of this page, or a number at the beginning of a line this indicates that there is something for you to do. But you will only generally find answers to the numbered instructions in the answer book.

Important words are written in **bold** when they are introduced for the first time.

"exceedingly tough mathematical problems (which the mathematically most advanced present day Western scientific world had spent huge lots of time, energy and money on and which even now it solves with the utmost difficulty and after vast labour involving large numbers of difficult, tedious and cumbersome 'steps' of working) can be easily and readily solved with the help of these ultra-easy Vedic Sutras (or athematical aphorisms).... in a few simple steps and by methods which can conscientiously be described as mere 'mental arithmetic'."

Bharati Krsna Tirthaji (1884–1960)
DISCOVERER OF VEDIC MATHEMATICS

1

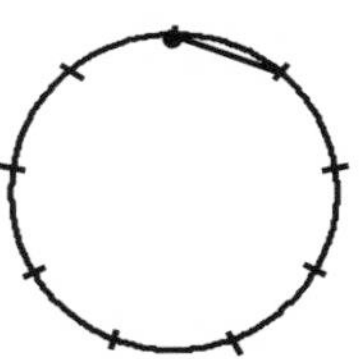

NIKHILAM MULTIPLICATION

The Sutra **Nikhilam** Navatascharaman Dasatah means *All from 9 and the Last from 10.* We have met this Sutra before.

Usually a sum like: 88 × 98
is considered especially difficult because of the large figures, 8 and 9.

But since the numbers 88 and 98 are close to the base of 100 we may think that there ought to be an easy way to find such a product.

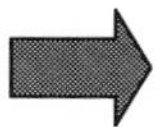

EXAMPLE 1

88 – 12	88 is 12 below 100, so we put –12 next to it,
98 – 2	98 is 2 below 100 so we put –2 next to it.
86 / 24	We call the 12 and 2 **deficiencies** as the numbers 88 and 98 are deficient from the unity of 100 by 12 and 2. ☞

The answer 8624 is in two parts: 86 and 24.
The 86 is found by taking one of the deficiencies from the other number: that is 88–2 = 86 or 98–12 = 86 (whichever you like),

and the 24 is simply the product of the deficiencies: 12 × 2 = 24.
So 88 × 98 = 8624. It could hardly be easier.

EXAMPLE 2

For 93 × 96 we get deficiencies of 7 and 4, so

$$\begin{array}{l} 93 - 07 \\ \underline{96 - 04} \\ \underline{89\ /\ 28} \end{array}$$

The differences from 100 are 7 and 4,
93 – 4 = 89 or 96 – 7 = 89, and 7 × 4 = 28.

In fact once we have got the deficiencies we apply *Vertically and Crosswise*: we **cross-subtract** to get the left-hand part of the answer and we **multiply vertically** in the right-hand column to get the right-hand part of the answer.

EXAMPLE 3

For 98 × 97:

$$\begin{array}{l} 98 - 02 \\ \underline{97 - 03} \\ \underline{95\ /\ 06} \end{array}$$

Note the zero inserted here: the numbers being multiplied are near to **100**, so **two** digits are required on the right, as in the other examples.

EXAMPLE 4

For 89 × 89:

$$\begin{array}{l} 89\ -\ 11 \\ \underline{89\ -\ 11} \\ \underline{78\ /\ {}_{1}21} \end{array} = \underline{7921}.$$

Here the numbers are each 11 below 100, and 11 × 11 = 121, a 3-figure number. The hundreds digit of this is therefore carried over to the left.

EXERCISE 1

Multiply the following:

a 94×94 **b** 97×89 **c** 87×99 **d** 87×98 **e** 87×95

f 95×95 **g** 79×96 **h** 98×96 **i** 92×99 **j** 88×88

k 97×56 **l** 97×63 **m** find a way to get 92×196?

The most efficient way to do these sums is to take one number and subtract the other deficiency from it. Then multiply the deficiencies together, mentally adjusting the first part of the answer if there is a carry figure.
This is so easy it is really just mental arithmetic.

EXERCISE 2

Multiply these numbers mentally, just write down the answer:

a 87 97	**b** 79 98	**c** 98 93	**d** 94 95	**e** 96 96	**f** 88 96	**g** 89 98
h 93 96	**i** 93 99	**j** 97 97	**k** 96 67	**l** 95 75	**m** 89 ?? 8544	find the missing numbers

OTHER BASES

EXAMPLE 5

Find 568×998.

In this sum the numbers are close to 1000, and the deficiencies are 432 and 2. The deficiency for 568 is found by applying the Sutra: *All from 9 and the Last from 10.*

☞

568 – 432
998 – 2
566 / 864

The method here is just the same, but we allow 3 figures on the right as the base is now 1000.

The number of spaces needed on the right is the number of 0's in the base number.

The differences of the numbers from 1000 are 432 and 2.
Then cross-subtracting: 568 – 2 = 566,
And vertically: 432 × 2 = 864.

 **EXAMPLE 6**

Find 58776 × 99998.

Even large numbers like this are easily and mentally multiplied by the same method.

58776 – 41224
99998 – 2
58774 / 82448

 **EXAMPLE 7**

Find 7 × 8.

In the Vedic system tables above 5×5 are not really essential:

7 – 3
8 – 2
5 / 6

Exactly the same method gives us 7 × 8 = 56.

 **EXERCISE 3**

Multiply the following mentally:

a 667 × 998	**b** 768 × 997	**c** 989 × 998	**d** 885 × 997
e 883 × 998	**f** 467 × 998	**g** 891 × 989	**h** 8888 × 9996
i 6999 × 9997	**j** 90909 × 99994	**k** 78989 × 99997	**l** 9876 × 9989

NUMBERS ABOVE THE BASE

Suppose now that the numbers are not both below a base number as in all the previous examples, but above the base.

EXAMPLE 8

103 × 104 = <u>10712</u>

$$\begin{array}{l} 103 + 3 \\ \underline{104 + 4} \\ \underline{107 / 12} \end{array}$$

This is even easier than the previous examples, but the method is just the same. The differences from the base are +3 and +4 because the numbers are now **above** the base.

103 + 4 = 107 or 104 + 3 = 107, and 4 × 3 = 12.

So now we **cross-add,** and multiply vertically.

EXAMPLE 9

12 × 13 = <u>156</u> (12+3=15, 2×3=6)

EXAMPLE 10

1234 × 1003 = <u>1237702</u> (1234+3=1237, 234×3=702)

EXAMPLE 11

10021 × 10002 = <u>100230042</u> (10021+2=10023, 0021×2=0042)

With a base of 10000 here we need 4 figures on the right.

❋ Check that you agree with all the examples above and then do the following exercise mentally.

EXERCISE 4

try these mentally

a 133 × 103	**b** 107 × 108	**c** 171 × 101	**d** 102 × 104
e 123 × 102	**f** 14 × 12	**g** 18 × 13	**h** 1222 × 1003
i 1051 × 1007	**j** 15111 × 10003	**k** 125 × 105	**l** 10034 × 10036

PROPORTIONATELY

The *Proportionately* formula considerably extends the range of this multiplication method.

EXAMPLE 12

213 × 203 = 43239

$$\begin{array}{rl} & 213 + 13 \\ & \underline{203 + \ \ 3} \\ 2 \times & \underline{216\ /\ 39} = \underline{43239} \end{array}$$

We observe here that the numbers are not near any of the bases used before: 10, 100, 1000 etc. But they are close to 200, with differences of 13 and 3 as shown above.

The usual procedure gives us 216/39 (213+3=216, 13×3=39).

Now since our base is 200 which is 100×2 we multiply **only the left-hand part** of the answer by 2 to get 43239.

EXAMPLE 13

29 × 28 = 812

The base is 30 (3×10),
and the deficiencies are –1 and –2.
Cross-subtracting gives 27,
then multiplying vertically on the right we get 2,
and finally 3×27 = 81.

$$\begin{array}{rl} & 29 - 1 \\ & \underline{28 - 2} \\ 3 \times & \underline{27\ /\ 2} = 812 \end{array}$$

So these are just like the previous sums but with an extra multiplication (of the left-hand side only) at the end.

EXAMPLE 14

Find 33 × 34.

In this example there is a carry figure:

$$\begin{array}{r} 33 + \ 3 \\ \underline{34 + \ 4} \\ \underline{3 \times 37\ /\ {}_1 2} \end{array} = 111\ /{}_1 2 = \underline{1122}$$

Note that since the right-hand side does not get multiplied by 3 we multiply the left-hand side by 3 before carrying the 1 over to the left.

EXAMPLE 15

$88 \times 49 = \frac{1}{2}(88 \times 98) = \frac{1}{2}(8624) = \underline{4312}$.

This example shows a different application of *Proportionately*.
In 88×49 the numbers are not both close to 100,
but since twice 49 is 98 we can find 88×98 and halve the answer at the end.

EXERCISE 5

Multiply mentally:

a 41×42 **b** 204×207 **c** 321×303 **d** 203×208 **e** 902×909

f 48×47 **g** 188×196 **h** 199×198 **i** 189×194 **j** 207×211

k 312×307 **l** 5003×5108 **m** 63×61 **n** 23×24 **o** 79×77

p 44×98 **q** 48×97 **r** 192×97

SQUARING NUMBERS NEAR A BASE

This is especially easy and is for squaring numbers which are near a base.
You will recall that squaring means that a number is multiplied by itself (like 96 × 96).
This method is described by the sub-formula: *Reduce (or increase) by the Deficiency and also set up the square*.

EXAMPLE 16

$96^2 = \underline{92/16}$

96 is 4 below 100, so we reduce 96 by 4, which gives us the first part of the answer, 92.
The last part is just $4^2 = \underline{16}$, as the formula says.

EXAMPLE 17

1006^2 = 1012/036

Here 1006 is increased by 6 to 1012, and $6^2 = 36$: but with a base of 1000 we need 3 figures on the right, so we put 036.

EXAMPLE 18

$304^2 = 3\times308/16$ = 92416

This is similar but because our base is 300 the left-hand part of the answer is multiplied by 3.

1 In this last example we can write 304^2 = 9/24/16 in which the answer has been split into three parts. Can you see how to get these parts from the figures in 304? Do you think this will always work with squaring numbers like: a0b?

EXERCISE 6

Square the following:

a 94	**b** 103	**c** 108	**d** 1012	**e** 98	**f** 88	**g** 91
h 10006	**i** 988	**j** 997	**k** 9999	**l** 9989	**m** 111	**n** 13
o 212	**p** 206	**q** 302	**r** 601	**s** 21	**t** 72	**u** 4012
v 511	**w** 987					

MULTIPLYING NUMBERS NEAR DIFFERENT BASES

EXAMPLE 19

9998 × 94 = 9398/12

Here the numbers are close to different bases: 10,000 and 100, and the deficiencies are –2 and –6. We write, or imagine, the sum set out as shown:

9998 – 2
94 – 6
9398 / 12

☞

❋ Can you see how the two parts of the answer are found?

It is important to line the numbers up as shown because the 6 is not subtracted from the 8, but from the 9 above the 4 in 94. That is, the second column from the left here.

So **9998 becomes 9398**.

Then multiply the deficiencies together: 2×6 = **12**.

Note that the number of figures in the right-hand part of the answer corresponds to the base of the lower number (94 is near 100, therefore there are 2 figures on the right).

You can see why this method works by looking at the sum 9998 × 9400, which is 100 times the sum done above:

$$\begin{array}{l} 9998 - 0002 \\ \underline{9400 - 600} \\ \underline{9398\ /\ 1200} \end{array}$$

❋ Check that you agree with this calculation.

Now we can see that since 9998 × 9400 = 93981200,
then 9998 × 94 = 939812.

This also shows why the 6 is subtracted in the second column from the left.

EXAMPLE 20

10007 × 1003 = <u>10037021</u>

Lining the numbers up:

$$\begin{array}{l} 10007 + 007 \\ \underline{1003 \quad + 003} \\ \underline{10037\ /\ 021} \end{array}$$

we see that we need three figures on the right and that the surplus, 3, is added in the 4th column, giving 10037.

EXERCISE 7

Find:

a 97 × 993 **b** 92 × 989 **c** 9988 × 98 **d** 9996 × 988

e 103 × 1015 **f** 106 × 1012 **g** 10034 × 102 **h** 1122 × 104

A SUMMARY

Here we can summarise the various methods of multiplication and squaring encountered so far.

1. Multiplying by 4, 8 etc. we can just double twice, 3 times etc. E.g. 37×4.
2. We can use doubling to extend the multiplication tables. E.g. 14×8.
3. We can multiply from left to right using *On the Flag*. E.g. 456×3.
4. We can square numbers ending in 5, using *By One More than the One Before*. E.g. 35^2.
5. With the same Sutra we can multiply numbers that have the same first digit and whose last figures add up to 10. E.g. 72×78.
6. We can use *All from 9 and the Last from 10* for multiplying numbers near a base.

   E.g. 98×88, 103×104, 203×204.
7. The same Sutra can be used for squaring numbers near a base. E.g. 97^2, 1006^2, 203^2.
8. And we can also multiply numbers near different bases. E.g. 998×97.

EXERCISE 8

The following exercise contains a mixture of all these different types of multiplication:

a 654 × 3	**b** 86 × 98	**c** 97 × 92	**d** 73 × 4	**e** 7 × 22
f 16 × 24	**g** 798 × 997	**h** 8899 × 9993	**i** 106^2	**j** 996^2
k 103 × 109	**l** 123 × 104	**m** 203 × 209	**n** 188 × 197	**o** 85^2
p 73 × 77	**q** 32 × 33	**r** 2004 × 2017	**s** 9997 × 98	**t** 1023 × 102
u 84 × 86	**v** 28 × 54	**w** 303 × 307	**x** 93^2	**y** 1011^2
z 403^2				

In Chapter 2 we have another special type of multiplication and in Chapter 7 we go on to the general method.

"His Majesty's Ministers, finding that Gulliver's stature exceeded theirs in the proportion of twelve to one, concluded from the similarity of their bodies that he must contain at least 1728 [or 12^3] of theirs, and must needs be rationed accordingly."

Johnathan Swift

FROM GULLIVER'S TRAVELS

2

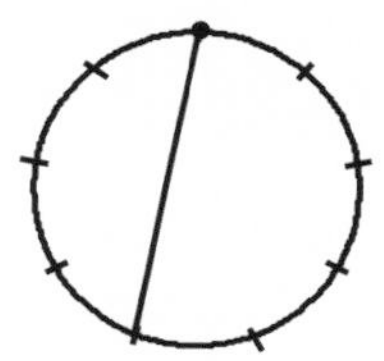

DOUBLING AND HALVING

There are many ways in which doubling and halving can be used beneficially.

 **EXAMPLE 1**

Find 35×22.

We can use doubling and halving in this sum to get a much easier sum.

We double 35 and halve 22 and this gives us 70×11 which has the same answer as 35×22.
So $35 \times 22 = 70 \times 11 = \underline{770}$.

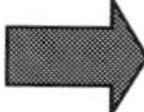 **EXAMPLE 2**

Find 35×64.

Doubling and halving gives us 70×32.
So we can use *On the Flag* to find 32×7 and put a 0 on the end.
So $35 \times 64 = 70 \times 32 = \underline{2240}$.

EXERCISE 1

Multiply the following:

a 15×18 **b** 15×24 **c** 46×15 **d** 82×35 **e** 66×15

f 124×45 **g** 15×54 **h** 55×16 **i** 75×18 **j** 446×15

k 132×35 **l** 85×18 **m** $16 \times 4\frac{1}{2}$ **n** $24 \times 3\frac{1}{2}$ **o** £4.50 × 32

p 44×225 (halve and double, twice) **q** 32×325

r 27×15 (double only the 15, multiply, and then halve the answer) **s** 41×35

MULTIPLYING BY 5, 50, 25

The numbers **2** and **5** are closely related because $2 \times 5 = 10$ and 10 is a base number.

> We can multiply by 5 by multiplying by 10 and halving the result.

EXAMPLE 3

Find 44×5.

We find half of 440, which is 220. So $44 \times 5 = \underline{220}$.

EXAMPLE 4

Find 87×5.

Half of 870 is 435. So $87 \times 5 = \underline{435}$.

Similarly $4.6 \times 5 =$ half of $46 = \underline{23}$.

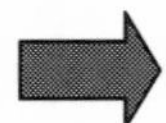

EXAMPLE 5

Find 27×50.

We multiply 27 by 100, and halve the result. Half of 2700 is 1350.
So $27 \times 50 = \underline{1350}$.

Similarly $5.2 \times 50 =$ half of $520 = \underline{260}$.

EXAMPLE 6

Find 82 × 25.
25 is half of half of 100, so to multiply a number by 25 we multiply it by 100 and halve twice.
So we find half of half of 8200, which is 2050. 82 × 25 = <u>2050</u>.

Similarly 6.8 × 25 = half of half of 680 = <u>170</u>.

EXERCISE 2

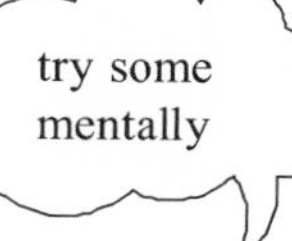

Multiply the following:

a 68 × 5 **b** 42 × 5 **c** 36 × 5 **d** 56 × 5 **e** 61 × 5 **f** 426 × 5

g 803 × 5 **h** 2468 × 5 **i** 46 × 50 **j** 864 × 50 **k** 223 × 50 **l** 202 × 50

m 72 × 25 **n** 48 × 25 **o** 85 × 25 **p** 808 × 25

EXERCISE 3

Multiply the following:

a 8.6 × 5 **b** 5.4 × 5 **c** 4.68 × 5 **d** 0.66 × 5 **e** 4.7 × 5

f 1.8 × 5 **g** 9.1 × 5 **h** 0.222 × 5 **i** 22.2 × 5 **j** 86.8 × 50

k 4.2 × 50 **l** 18.6 × 50 **m** 6.24 × 50 **n** 4.444 × 50 **o** 34.56 × 50

p 2.8 × 25 **q** 2.4 × 25 **r** 0.88 × 25 **s** 40.6 × 25 **t** 0.08 × 25

DIVIDING BY 5, 50, 25

EXAMPLE 7

Find 85 ÷ 5 = 17.

For dividing by 5 we can double and then divide by 10.

So 85 is doubled to 170, and dividing by 10 gives 17.

EXAMPLE 8

665 ÷ 5 = 133, since 665 doubled is 1330.

An alternative method with a different Sutra may be used here. Since there are two fives in every ten, in the sum 85 ÷ 5 you may decide there are 16 5's in the 80 and therefore 17 5's in 85. In other words you would double the 8 and add 1 on. Which Sutra do you think might be involved here?

EXAMPLE 9

73 ÷ 5 = 14.6.
Similarly here double 73 is 146, and dividing by 10 gives 14.6.

EXERCISE 4

Divide by 5:

a 65	**b** 135	**c** 375	**d** 470	**e** 505
f 4005	**g** 1235	**h** 7070	**i** 7200	**j** 885
k 195	**l** 7770	**m** 64	**n** 49	**o** 52
p 22.2	**q** 32.1	**r** 54.3	**s** 4.3	**t** 6.23
u 7.81	**v** 0.44	**w** 0.97	**x** 0.099	

EXAMPLE 10

Find 750 ÷ 50.

Since 50 is half of 100 dividing by 50 involves doubling and dividing by 100.

Doubling 750 gives 1500, and dividing this by 100 gives 15.
So 750 ÷ 50 = <u>15</u>.

Again the alternative Sutra *The Ultimate and Twice the Penultimate* tells us to double the 7 and add on the one extra 50, giving 15 again.

EXAMPLE 11

54.32 ÷ 50 = <u>1.0864</u>.
Doubling 54.32 gives 108.64, and dividing by 100 gives 1.0864.

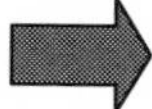

EXAMPLE 12

Find 425 ÷ 25.

25 is a quarter of 100 so to divide by 25 we can double twice and divide by 100.100.

Doubling 425 gives 850, and doubling this gives 1700.
Dividing by 100 then gives us 17. So 425 ÷ 25 = <u>17</u>.

EXERCISE 5

Divide by 50:	**a** 650	**b** 1250	**c** 3300	**d** 12000	**e** 7600	**f** 5850
	g 65.2	**h** 22.33	**i** 4.3	**j** 8.8	**k** 44	**l** 77
Divide by 25:	**m** 225	**n** 550	**o** 375	**p** 7050	**q** 1525	**r** 2375
	s 32.1	**t** 2.02	**u** 81.5	**v** 44	**w** 137	**x** 6

"It is interesting to see that modern Mathematics starts from the field of diversity and locates its source in the field of unity; whereas Vedic Mathematics remains in the state of unity and deals with the whole structure of unmanifest diversity from the state of unity; and as the basis of all diversity is unity, Vedic Mathematics has its influence on every level of diversity."

Maharishi Mahesh Yogi
FOUNDER OF TRANSCENDENTAL MEDITATION

3

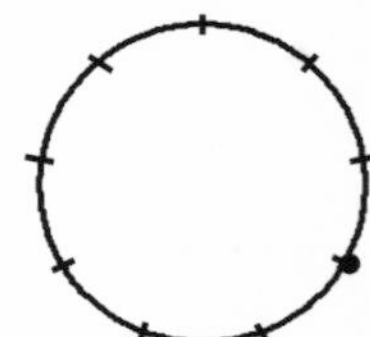

FRACTIONS

A fraction shows how a part is related to a whole.

Fractions are written like $\frac{4}{7}$ where the top number is called the **numerator**, and the bottom number is called the **denominator**.

And we say "four sevenths", or "four over seven".

TOP-HEAVY FRACTIONS

A fraction like $\frac{7}{4}$ is **top-heavy** because the numerator is greater than the denominator.
They are also called improper fractions or vulgar fractions.

Top-heavy fractions are always greater than a whole one.

In the case of $\frac{7}{4}$ since $\frac{4}{4}$=1 whole, $\frac{7}{4}$ must be $1\frac{3}{4}$ (4 quarters + 3 quarters).

A number like $1\frac{3}{4}$ is called a **mixed number** because it is a mixture between a whole number and a fraction.

In fact we can always convert a top-heavy fraction into a mixed number by dividing the numerator by the denominator.

EXAMPLE 1

Convert $\frac{33}{5}$ into a mixed number.

We divide 5 into 33 and get 6 remainder 3, so there are 6 whole ones.

So $\frac{33}{5} = 6\frac{3}{5}$.

EXAMPLE 2

Convert $3\frac{4}{5}$ to a top-heavy fraction.

This is the reverse process, and we need to know how many fifths in $3\frac{4}{5}$.

Since each whole has 5 fifths there will be 15 fifths in 3 whole ones, and adding the 4 fifths gives 19 fifths altogether.

So $3\frac{4}{5} = \frac{19}{5}$.

EXAMPLE 3

Convert $7\frac{2}{3}$ to a top-heavy fraction.

There are 21 thirds in 7 whole ones, adding 2 more gives $7\frac{2}{3} = \frac{23}{3}$.

The quick way here is to multiply 3 by 7 and add the 2 on, this gives 23 more easily.

Similarly with Example 2: $5\times3 + 4 = 19$.

EXERCISE 1

Convert the following top-heavy fractions into mixed numbers:

a $\frac{9}{4}$ **b** $\frac{23}{3}$ **c** $\frac{19}{3}$ **d** $\frac{7}{2}$ **e** $\frac{15}{3}$ **f** $\frac{36}{5}$

g $\frac{11}{6}$ **h** $\frac{60}{7}$ **i** $\frac{300}{70}$ **j** $\frac{30}{9}$ **k** $\frac{36}{4}$ **l** $\frac{123}{30}$

Convert the following into top-heavy fractions:

m $3\frac{3}{4}$ **n** $5\frac{2}{3}$ **o** $9\frac{1}{7}$ **p** $2\frac{4}{9}$ **q** $1\frac{7}{10}$ **r** $11\frac{2}{5}$

s $1\frac{5}{6}$ **t** $8\frac{8}{9}$ **u** $20\frac{19}{20}$

FINDING A FRACTION OF A NUMBER

We have already had questions like finding $\frac{3}{4}$ of something.

EXAMPLE 4

Find $\frac{3}{5}$ of 20.

We first find $\frac{1}{5}$ of 20 by dividing it by 5. This gives us 4.

Then if $\frac{1}{5}$ of 20 is 4, $\frac{3}{5}$ of 20 must be three times as much, which is <u>12</u>.

We can also multiply by the numerator first, and then divide by the denominator, we get the same answer:

$$\frac{3}{5} \text{ of } 20 = \frac{1}{5} \text{ of } 60 = 12.$$

Note also that since "3 of 20" means 3 20's, or 60, "3 of 20" is the same as 3×20.

So also $\frac{3}{5}$ of 20 is exactly the same as $\frac{3}{5}\times 20$.

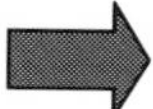

EXAMPLE 5

Find $\frac{5}{6} \times 2$.

This example shows that it is sometimes better to multiply by the numerator first.

$\frac{5}{6} \times 2 = \frac{10}{6}$.

EXAMPLE 6

Find $\frac{2}{3} \times £1.20$.

Since $\frac{1}{3}$ of £1.20 is £0.40, $\frac{2}{3}$ of £1.20 must be <u>£0.80 or 80p</u>.

> To find a fraction of a number we either divide the number by the denominator and then multiply by the numerator, or we multiply the number by the numerator first and then divide by the denominator.

EXAMPLE 7

Find $\frac{7}{4} \times 4.4$.

$4.4 \div 4 = 1.1$
$7 \times 1.1 = \underline{\mathbf{7.7}}$

The alternative method of multiplying by the numerator first is not easier here: we would have to multiply 4.4 by 7, and then divide by 4.

The last example shows us that we can still find a fraction of something even if the numerator is greater than the denominator. Since $\frac{7}{4} = 1\frac{3}{4}$ we have found $1\frac{3}{4}$ of 4.4.

EXAMPLE 8

$1\frac{2}{5} \times 15 = \frac{7}{5} \times 15 = 7 \times 3 = \underline{\mathbf{21}}$ (since $1\frac{2}{5} = \frac{7}{5}$).

Finding a fraction of a number comes under the *Proportionately* Sutra, *Anurupyena*.

EXERCISE 2

Find (give answers cancelled and as mixed numbers where appropriate):

a $\frac{2}{5}$ of 30 **b** $\frac{7}{5}$ of 80 **c** $\frac{4}{7} \times 2$ **d** $\frac{5}{6} \times 20$ **e** $\frac{7}{10} \times 7$ **f** $\frac{2}{3} \times 33$

g $\frac{7}{8} \times 40$ **h** $\frac{5}{3} \times 12$ **i** $\frac{9}{2} \times 40$ **j** $\frac{11}{3} \times 3$ **k** $\frac{3}{7} \times 140$ **l** $\frac{30}{17} \times 340$

m $\frac{4}{10} \times 30$ **n** $\frac{6}{15} \times 30$ **o** $2\frac{2}{3} \times 5$ **p** $1\frac{1}{8} \times 40$

EQUIVALENT FRACTIONS

If you look at your answers to sums **a**, **m** and **n** in the last exercise you should find that they are all the same.

This suggests that the fractions $\frac{2}{5}$, $\frac{4}{10}$ and $\frac{6}{15}$ are all equivalent (the same).

This is in fact true and we can see why by looking at the diagrams below:

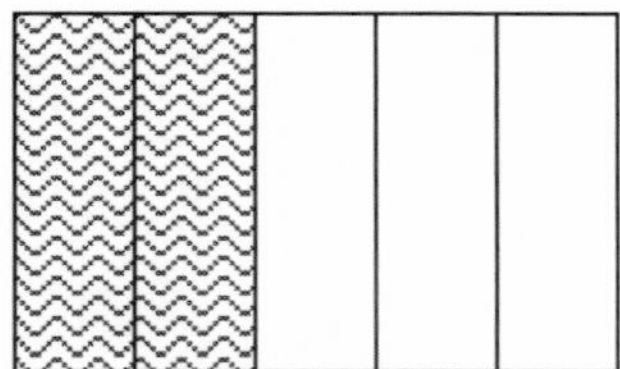

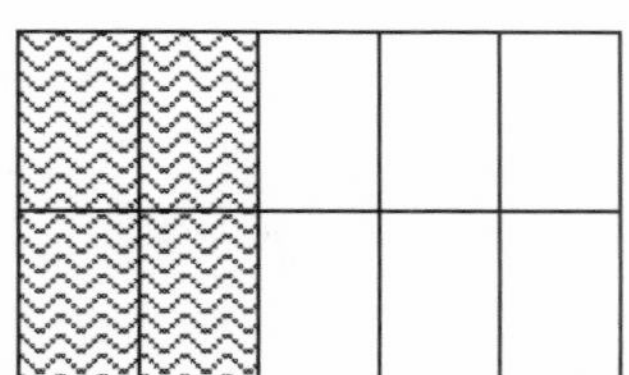

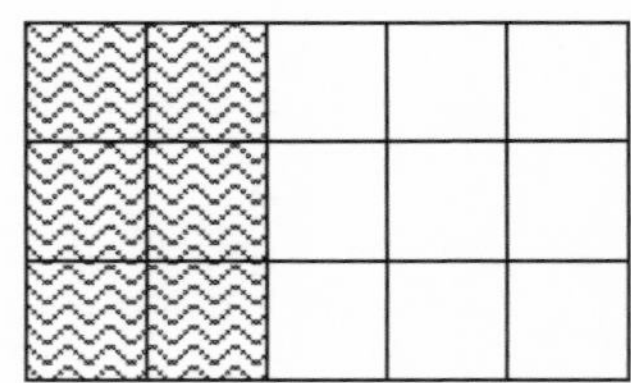

The amount shaded is the same in each diagram so they all show $\frac{2}{5}$.

But the extra line in the middle diagram shows that $\frac{4}{10}$ is the same as $\frac{2}{5}$.

Notice also that the 4 and the 10 in $\frac{4}{10}$ are twice the 2 and the 5 in $\frac{2}{5}$.

So we can get $\frac{4}{10}$ by multiplying the numerator and denominator of $\frac{2}{5}$ by 2: $\frac{2}{5} = \frac{4}{10}$.

Similarly we can get $\frac{6}{15}$ by multiplying numerator and denominator of $\frac{2}{5}$ by 3: $\frac{2}{5} = \frac{6}{15}$.

In fact we can generate as many fractions as we like from a fraction by multiplying the top and bottom by any number we like.

If we multiply $\frac{2}{5}$ on the top and bottom by 2, 3, 4, 5, ... etc. we get

$\frac{4}{10}, \frac{6}{15}, \frac{8}{20}, \frac{10}{25}$ . . . . . etc..

We call these **equivalent fractions**.
They also come under the *Proportionately* formula.

EXAMPLE 9

Give 5 fractions equivalent to $\frac{3}{4}$.

Multiplying $\frac{3}{4}$ (top and bottom) by 2, 3, 4,5 and 6 we get: $\frac{3}{4} = \frac{6}{8}, \frac{9}{12}, \frac{12}{16}, \frac{15}{20}, \frac{18}{24}$.

EXAMPLE 10

Which of the fractions $\frac{8}{12}, \frac{10}{18}, \frac{16}{24}, \frac{14}{21}$ are equivalent to $\frac{2}{3}$?

$\frac{8}{12}$ is equivalent to $\frac{2}{3}$ because if we multiply **2 and 3** by 4 we get **8 and 12**.

But $\frac{10}{18}$ is not equivalent to $\frac{2}{3}$ because we would need to multiply the top by 5 and the bottom by 6.

$\frac{16}{24}$ we can get from $\frac{2}{3}$ by multiplying top and bottom by 8, so it is equivalent, and $\frac{14}{21}$ is also equivalent since we can multiply the $\frac{2}{3}$ by 7.

EXERCISE 3

Give 4 equivalent fractions for each of the following:

a $\frac{3}{5}$ **b** $\frac{1}{4}$ **c** $\frac{7}{9}$ **d** $\frac{5}{6}$ **e** $\frac{3}{2}$ **f** $\frac{8}{10}$

g Which of the following fractions are equivalent to $\frac{4}{5}$? $\frac{12}{15}, \frac{8}{12}, \frac{6}{10}, \frac{20}{25}, \frac{16}{20}$

h Two of the following fractions are equivalent: which are they? $\frac{1}{5}, \frac{2}{12}, \frac{3}{12}, \frac{4}{20}, \frac{5}{10}$

i Two of the following fractions are equivalent: which are they? $\frac{5}{7}, \frac{6}{8}, \frac{7}{10}, \frac{8}{10}, \frac{9}{12}$

SIMPLIFYING FRACTIONS

We can find as many fractions as we like equivalent to a given fraction, but there is always one that is simpler than all the others.

Given $\frac{2}{3}, \frac{4}{6}, \frac{6}{9}, \frac{8}{12}, \frac{15}{15}$ which are equivalent, $\frac{2}{3}$ is the simplest of them all.

> If we have to obtain the simplest fraction equal to a given fraction we look for the **highest common factor** of numerator and denominator and divide them by this number.

EXAMPLE 11

Simplify $\frac{10}{15}$.

Since 10 and 15 can both be divided by 5, we divide them both by 5 and say: $\frac{10}{15} = \frac{2}{3}$.

EXAMPLE 12

Simplify $\frac{16}{12}$.

The HCF of 16 and 12 is 4, so we divide by 4.
We choose the largest divisor.
So $\frac{16}{12} = \frac{4}{3}$

Had we divided 16 and 12 by 2 instead we would get $\frac{16}{12} = \frac{8}{6}$ which is correct but does not give the simplest fraction. We would then need to observe that 6 and 8 can both be divided by 2, and then dividing we get $\frac{16}{12} = \frac{8}{6} = \frac{4}{3}$.
This gives the same answer, but it is a bit longer.

Simplifying fractions like this is also called **cancelling down**, or putting into **lowest terms**.
It comes under the Vedic formula *If the Samuccaya is the Same, it is Zero,* which simply means that any common factor can be cancelled out.

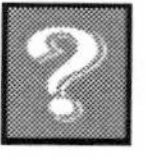

EXERCISE 4

Cancel down the following fractions (converting to mixed numbers where appropriate).
Check your answer each time to see if it can be divided further:

a $\frac{4}{10}$ **b** $\frac{6}{9}$ **c** $\frac{15}{20}$ **d** $\frac{44}{55}$ **e** $\frac{14}{21}$ **f** $\frac{9}{6}$

g $\frac{25}{10}$ **h** $\frac{2}{18}$ **i** $\frac{3}{18}$ **j** $\frac{4}{18}$ **k** $\frac{6}{18}$ **l** $\frac{8}{18}$

m $\frac{10}{18}$ **n** $\frac{18}{18}$ **o** $\frac{25}{30}$ **p** $\frac{27}{30}$ **q** $\frac{16}{24}$ **r** $\frac{63}{54}$

FINDING WHAT FRACTION ONE NUMBER IS OF ANOTHER

If we compare the numbers 1 and 4 we see that 4 is 4 times 1, and that 1 is a quarter of 4.

If we are asked what fraction 1 is of 4, the answer is 1 is ¼ of 4.

EXAMPLE 13

What fraction is 9 of 12?

The fraction is $\frac{9}{12}$ which cancels down to $\frac{3}{4}$. So 9 is $\frac{3}{4}$ of 12.

We simply put the first number on top of the fraction and the second on the bottom, and cancel if possible.

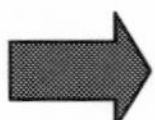

EXAMPLE 14

What fraction is x pence of y pence?

The answer is $\frac{x}{y}$.

EXAMPLE 15

What fraction is 10 pence of £3?

Here we must be careful: we should not mix up the units.

Converting the £3 into 300 pence we write the fraction as $\frac{10}{300}$ or $\frac{1}{30}$.

EXERCISE 5

Cancel down your answers to the following questions where appropriate:

a What fraction is 5 of 20?

b What fraction is 2 of 17?

c What fraction is 20p of £1?

d What fraction is £1.20 of £1.44?

e What fraction is 1m 20cm of 6m?

f What fraction is 10 minutes of 1½ hours?

g What fraction is 600m of 3km?

h What **fraction of** 1 minute is 15 seconds?

i What fraction of 3 feet is 4 inches?

"Great fleas have little fleas
upon their backs to bite 'em.
Little fleas have lesser fleas
and so on ad infinitum."

4

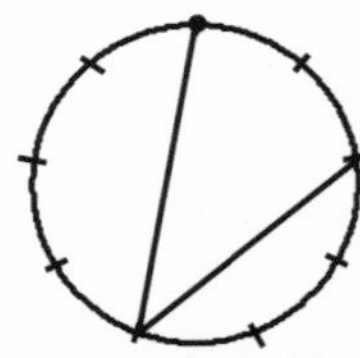

SPIRALS

The spiral is a very beautiful and important shape. It occurs frequently in nature, in shells, flowers and the structure of plants.

There are different kinds of spirals. The one found in nature is usually the **equiangular spiral**.
The principle behind the growth of an equiangular spiral is that the shape is constant: any part of the curve is an exact enlargement of an earlier part. As the creature that lives in a shell enlarges its home it keeps it the same shape but bigger.

THE ISOSCELES RIGHT-ANGLED TRIANGLE

There is only one shape of triangle which is both isosceles and right-angled.

What will the angles be in a triangle which is both isosceles and right-angled?

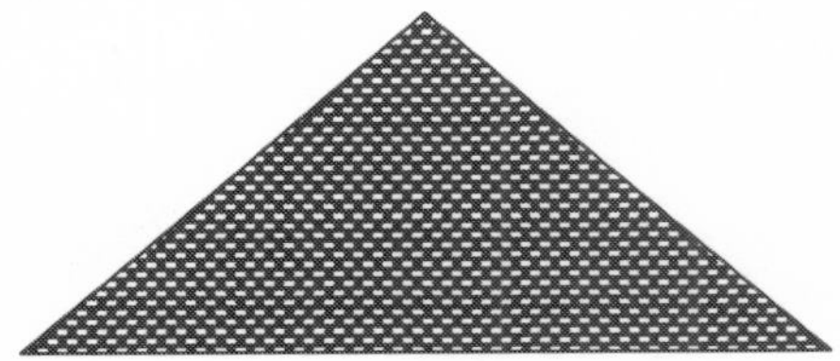

Suppose the top angle here is 90° then the other two angles must be the equal ones. And since we can see the triangle as one half of a square the two base angles must be 45° each.
Though the shape of this triangle is fixed its size and its position may vary.

For example both of these triangles are isosceles right-angled triangles

The longest side of a right-angled triangle is called the **hypotenuse.**

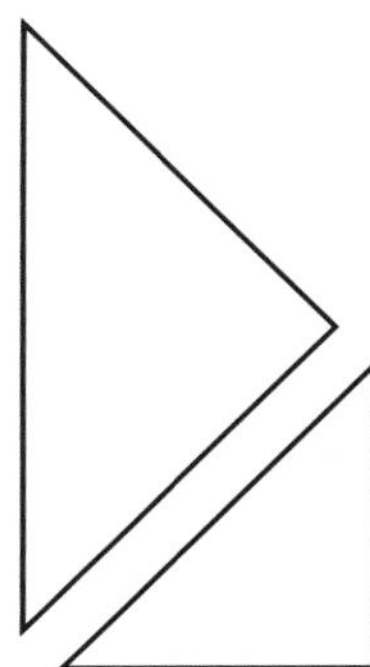

Note the way the larger triangle almost stands on the hypotenuse of the smaller triangle.

EXERCISE 1

a Take a sheet of graph paper and with the longer edge at the bottom draw a horizontal line 1cm long on one of the bold lines about 8cm from the left edge and about 8cm from the top edge.

b This line is the base of an isosceles right-angled triangle with the right angle at the right end of the line. Complete the triangle.

c Another isosceles right-angled triangle must now be drawn with its base on the hypotenuse of the first triangle (rather like the diagram above, but the lines will touch).
Be careful and use the lines on your page to guide you.

d The second triangle is an enlarged version of the first one and is joined onto it.
We are going to repeat this procedure: add a third triangle to the hypotenuse of the second one. It must be the same shape as the others, with the right angle on the right of the base.
You may prefer to turn your sheet so that the right-hand edge is at the bottom.

☞

e Continue this until you have 8 triangles altogether. You should then have a kind of spiral shape.

f The next triangle will go off your page so we cannot draw any bigger triangles. It is possible however to draw some smaller ones. See if you can draw a triangle below the first one so that its hypotenuse is the base of the first triangle. If you can do this draw in some more even smaller triangles.

g Note how the base of each triangle is rotated 45° to become the larger base of the next triangle. Put a dot at the top corner of each triangle. Draw a smooth spiral through all these dots and when it looks right go over it with a coloured pencil.

This shows the kind of equiangular growth discussed at the beginning of this chapter.

SPIRALS FROM SQUARES

EXERCISE 2

a On a new graph page draw a square with sides 2cm near the centre of the sheet. Use the bold lines on the graph paper. We will call this Square 3. In your book write down the area of Square 3.

b Put a dot in the middle of each side of your square and join them up to make a diamond shape. Is this shape also a square?

c The sides of your smaller shape are equal and so are the four angles, so it must be a square. Call this Square 2. What is the area of this square?

d Looking carefully at the four squares inside the larger square you should see that the diagonals you drew inside it cut each of these four squares in half. It follows that the inner square has half the area of the outer one, that is $2cm^2$.
Draw another square inside Square 2 by joining the middle of the sides of Square 2. By the same logic as above the area of this square must also be half of the area of Square 2. So its area is $1\ cm^2$.
Check with your ruler that this is correct.

☞

e Now we have 3 squares inside each other. Starting with the inner square (Square 1) it is as though Square 1 is rotating and growing to become the next square. Draw a fourth square outside Square 3 so that the corners of Square 3 are in the middle of each side.

f Add another square outside Square 4 and continue doing this as far as you can. You will probably have 9 squares.

g Complete a list of the areas of each square in your book.

h Next we can draw in a spiral. Put a dot in the top left-hand corner of Square 1. The first spiral will go clockwise from here. Imagine Square 1 turning clockwise and growing so that it becomes Square 2: the dot will now be at the top of Square 2. Put a dot there. Next Square turns onto Square 3 and the dot is now at the top right of Square 3. Continue to add dots until you arrive at a dot in the top left corner of Square 9. Join the dots (first with a pencil and then in colour) with a smooth spiral curve.

i Now you have a choice: you can either draw in three more clockwise spirals starting at each of the other three corners of Square 1, or you can start again at the top left-hand corner of Square 1 but turn anti-clockwise instead of clockwise.

AN INFINITE SUM

EXERCISE 3

a On a fresh graph page draw a square 16cm by 16cm.
The method we are going to use here is to **halve a shape** (a square or rectangle), **put a dot in the centre of one part and halve the other part**, and keep repeating this.

b Halve your square by drawing a vertical line down the middle and put a dot in the exact centre of the left-hand half.

c Halve the right-hand rectangle (by drawing a horizontal line) and put a dot in the centre of the upper half.

☞

d Halve the lower square (by drawing a vertical line) and put a dot in the centre of the right-hand half.

e Halve the left-hand rectangle, and put a dot in the centre of the lower half. Continue this process, you can go back to **b** above if you like and keep repeating steps b,c,d,e until you have at least 9 dots.

f Next you can carefully draw in the spiral that goes through all the dots in order.

g Now suppose that the side of the large square is called 1 unit. This means that the area of the large square is 1 square unit. Each dot you have drawn is in the centre of a square or rectangle. Starting with the large rectangle on the left write down the area of each shape which has a dot in its centre. The first rectangle, for example must have an area of ½ a square unit.

h Each area will be half of the previous area and we can see that since the spiral goes on forever there are an infinite number of areas.
The area of the big square is the total of the areas of all the shapes inside it.
This is: $\frac{1}{2}+\frac{1}{4}+\frac{1}{8}+\frac{1}{16}+\frac{1}{32}+\frac{1}{64}+\frac{1}{128}+...$ where the dots mean that the fractions go on forever.
But since the area of the big square is 1 we can write:

$$\frac{1}{2}+\frac{1}{4}+\frac{1}{8}+\frac{1}{16}+\frac{1}{32}+\frac{1}{64}+\frac{1}{128}+\frac{1}{256}+... = 1,$$

and we have found the total of an infinite number of fractions!

"I often feel, especially when I am alone, that I dwell in another world. Ideas of numbers take on a life of their own. Suddenly, questions of any kind rise before my eyes with answers.

Ferrol

A CALCULATING PRODIGY

5

FRACTIONS AND DECIMALS

In this chapter we are going to study how fractions and decimals are related, and how to convert from one to the other.

CONVERTING DECIMALS TO FRACTIONS

EXAMPLE 1

A decimal like 0.6 is easily converted into a fraction: we know that $0.6 = \frac{6}{10}$

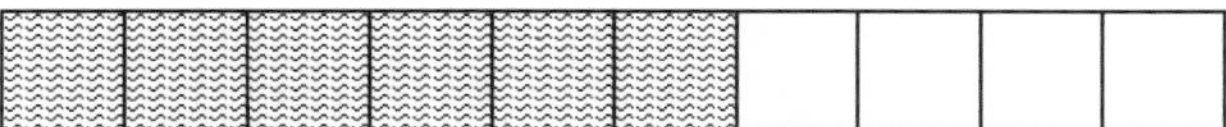

And this can be cancelled down: $\frac{6}{10} = \frac{3}{5}$.

So the simplest fraction equal to 0.6 is $\frac{3}{5}$.

EXAMPLE 2

Convert 0.05 to a fraction.

Since the 5 is in the hundredths position: $0.05 = \frac{5}{100} = \frac{1}{20}$

EXAMPLE 3

Convert 0.15 to a fraction.
The 1 here is in the tenths position and the 5 is in the hundredths position.
But we can think of the 1 tenth as being 10 hundredths, rather like this:

$$0.15 = 0.0_15$$

then we can see that $0.15 = \frac{15}{100} = \frac{3}{20}$.

EXAMPLE 4

Convert 23.4 to a fraction.

Here we think of the whole part and the fraction separately:
we have 23 whole ones and $0.4 = \frac{4}{10} = \frac{2}{5}$. So $23.4 = 23\frac{2}{5}$.

EXERCISE 1

Convert the following into fractions (cancel down as much as possible):

a 0.3 **b** 0.4 **c** 0.04 **d** 0.07 **e** 0.005 **f** 0.0001

g 0.25 **h** 0.35 **i** 0.16 **j** 0.17 **k** 0.055 **l** 0.032

m 0.0011 **n** 1.3 **o** 2.5 **p** 3.7 **q** 8.01 **r** 2.2

s 20.1 **t** 10.01 **u** 0.123 **v** 0.222 **w** 0.444

CHANGING FRACTIONS TO DECIMALS

EXAMPLE 5

Convert $\frac{7}{100}$ and $\frac{17}{100}$ and $\frac{17}{50}$ into decimal form.

We know that $\frac{7}{100} = \mathbf{0.07}$ and $\frac{17}{100} = \mathbf{0.17}$ and $\frac{17}{50} = \frac{34}{100} = \mathbf{0.34}$.

This method works well for fractions which have base numbers (10, 100, 1000 etc.) in the denominator, or which can easily be multiplied up as in the 3rd case above.

EXAMPLE 6

Convert $\frac{3}{4}$ into a decimal.

We know that a fraction is unchanged by multiplying or dividing the top and bottom by the same number. For example $\frac{2}{3} = \frac{4}{6}$ and $\frac{20}{25} = \frac{4}{5}$.

If we divide the top and bottom of $\frac{3}{4}$ by 4 (the denominator) we get $\frac{3 \div 4}{4 \div 4}$ which is $\frac{3 \div 4}{1}$ which is just $3 \div 4$.

> In other words we can convert a fraction into a decimal by dividing the numerator by the denominator.

So **we write 3 as 3.00** and divide.

Dividing 3 by 4 gives 0 remainder 3: $4\overline{)3.{}_{3}0\ 0}$ giving $0.$

Next we divide 4 into 30 giving 7 remainder 2: $4\overline{)3.{}_{3}0\ {}_{2}0}$ giving 0.7

☞

Finally 4 into 20 goes 5 times: $4\overline{)3._{3}0_{2}0}$

$0.\,7\,\,5$

The division stops here and so we have $\frac{3}{4} = \underline{0.75}$

Alternatively, we can multiply the top and bottom of $\frac{3}{4}$ by 25 to get

$$\frac{3\times25}{4\times25} = \frac{75}{100} = \underline{\mathbf{0.75}}$$

EXAMPLE 7

Convert $\frac{7}{5}$ into a decimal.

We set up the sum: $5\overline{)7.00}$ and continue just as in ordinary division until there is nothing left to divide.

It is not important how many zeros we put after the 7, we can always add more as we go along if we need to.

The division gives: $5\overline{)\ 7._{2}0\ 0}$

$1.\,4$ so $\frac{7}{5} = \underline{\mathbf{1.4}}$

An alternative method here would be to change $\frac{7}{5}$ to $\frac{14}{10}$ which equals 1.4.

EXERCISE 2

Convert to decimals without using division:

a $\frac{9}{10}$ **b** $\frac{43}{100}$ **c** $\frac{3}{50}$ **d** $\frac{36}{1000}$ **e** $\frac{3}{20}$ **f** $\frac{13}{5}$ **g** $\frac{1}{25}$

Convert to decimals using division:

h $\frac{3}{5}$ **i** $\frac{5}{4}$ **j** $\frac{3}{8}$ **k** $\frac{13}{8}$ **l** $\frac{31}{4}$ **m** $\frac{125}{8}$

COMPARING FRACTIONS AND DECIMALS

EXAMPLE 8

Which is greater: 0.4 or $\frac{3}{8}$?

To compare these we convert $\frac{3}{8}$ to a decimal.

We get $\frac{3}{8}$ = 0.375 by division and we can now see that this is less than 0.4 (if this not clear think of 0.4 as 0.400, then 375 is clearly less than 400).

EXERCISE 3

Decide in each case which is greater:

a $\frac{21}{50}$ or 0.4 **b** $\frac{13}{20}$ or 0.62 **c** $\frac{7}{4}$ or 1.8 **d** $\frac{23}{50}$ or $\frac{9}{20}$

e $\frac{3}{5}$ or 0.71 **f** $\frac{9}{8}$ or 1.2 **g** $\frac{4}{5}$ or 0.75 **h** $\frac{7}{2}$ or $\frac{17}{5}$

i Arrange the following in ascending order: 0.2 $\frac{1}{4}$ 0.65 $\frac{3}{5}$.

All the fractions dealt with above give decimals which divide exactly.
They are called **Terminating Decimals**.

RECURRING DECIMALS

EXAMPLE 9

Convert $\frac{1}{3}$ to a decimal.

On division we find: $3\,\overline{)1.{}_10\,{}_10\,{}_10}$

0. 3 3 3. . .

We find here that the decimal goes on and on, giving an endless series of 3's.

Although the 3's go on forever it is possible to express this by writing: $\frac{1}{3} = 0.\dot{3}$. The dot on top of the 3 indicates that it repeats itself endlessly.
This type of decimal is called a **Recurring Decimal**.

EXAMPLE 10

Convert $\frac{7}{6}$ to a decimal.

Division gives: $6\overline{)7.{}_10\,{}_40\,{}_40}$
$1.\,1\,6\,6\ldots$

Here we find that a 6 repeats itself indefinitely after the first two figures of the answer.

So we write $\frac{7}{6} = 1.1\dot{6}$.

Similarly $\frac{8}{300}$ can be found by first dividing numerator and denominator by 100 to give $\frac{0.08}{3}$.

EXERCISE 4

Convert to recurring decimals:

a $\frac{2}{3}$ **b** $\frac{4}{9}$ **c** $\frac{1}{6}$ **d** $\frac{13}{9}$ **e** $\frac{412}{3}$ **f** $\frac{4}{15}$ **g** $\frac{7}{90}$ **h** $\frac{13}{300}$

Whether or not a decimal recurs or terminates depends only on the denominator: e.g. since $\frac{1}{4}$ terminates, so will $\frac{3}{4}, \frac{7}{4}$.

Similarly $\frac{1}{3}$ gives a recurring decimal, so $\frac{2}{3}, \frac{4}{3}, \frac{5}{3}$ etc. will also be the recurring type, but $\frac{3}{3}, \frac{6}{3}$ etc. will not recur because $\frac{3}{3} = 1$, $\frac{6}{3} = 2$ and so on, so given a fraction it is best to first check it is in its lowest terms.

BLOCK RECURRERS

Recurring decimals may be of the type that recur as above, or they may recur in another way.

EXAMPLE 11

Convert $\frac{2}{7}$ into a decimal.

We divide as usual:

$$\begin{array}{l} 7\,\underline{)2._{2}0_{6}0_{4}0_{5}0_{1}0_{3}0_{2}0_{6}0} \\ \quad\mathbf{0.\ 2\,8\,5\ \ 7\,1\,4\ldots.} \end{array}$$

We find the numbers 285714 appearing, then a remainder of 2. Since 20÷7 is how we started the division we find the same 2 which started the decimal coming up again.

It follows that the same six figures will repeat themselves: we have a block of figures repeating themselves.

We write the answer to this as: $\frac{2}{7}=0.\dot{2}8571\dot{4}$ we have two dots here,

to show that all the figures, from the first to the last, repeat in a block.

EXERCISE 5

0.142857142857142857142857142857......

Convert to decimals:

a $\frac{1}{7}$ **b** $\frac{3}{7}$ **c** $\frac{4}{7}$ **d** $\frac{5}{7}$ **e** $\frac{6}{7}$

f What do you notice about the decimals for $\frac{1}{7}$ to $\frac{6}{7}$?

g $\frac{1}{11}$ **h** $\frac{2}{11}$ **i** $\frac{3}{11}$ **j** $\frac{1}{13}$ **k** $\frac{2}{13}$

l What do you notice about the decimals for $\frac{1}{11}$, $\frac{2}{11}$, $\frac{3}{11}$?

m What do you think the decimals for $\frac{4}{11}$ and $\frac{5}{11}$ will be?

Block recurrers can be plotted on the 9 point circle, each denominator having its own individual pattern or patterns. ☞

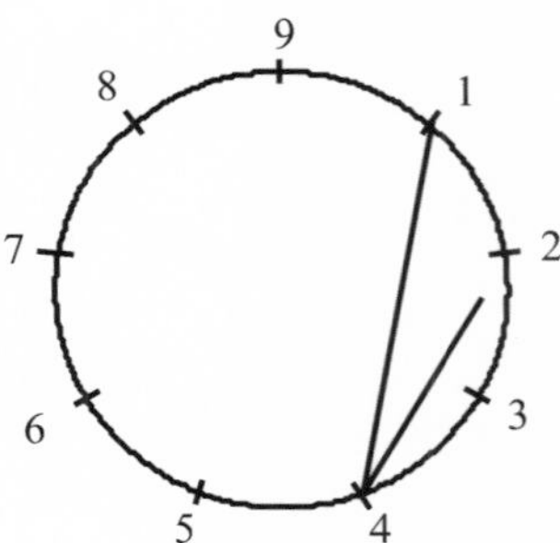

n Complete the pattern for $\frac{1}{7} = 0.\dot{1}4285\dot{7}$ on a copy of the diagram above by drawing lines from 1 to 4, then 4 to 2, then 2 to 8, then 8 to 5, then 5 to 7, as shown in the sequence 142857.
Then join 7 to 1 because the sequence is actually 14285714285714. . . .

o Compare this pattern with the patterns for $\frac{2}{7}$, $\frac{3}{7}$.

p Draw the pattern on a 9 point circle for $\frac{1}{13}$ (remember 0 and 9 are both at the same point)

q Draw the pattern (on the right-hand circle above) for $\frac{2}{13}$.

You may have noticed with the decimals for $\frac{1}{7}$ to $\frac{6}{7}$ that the pattern is the same.
Also the figures 14285714285714 . . . in the decimal for $\frac{1}{7}$ is the same sequence as for the other fractions, only the starting point is different.
Since 142857 has **six figures** this can account for the **six fractions** from $\frac{1}{7}$ to $\frac{6}{7}$.

However if you consider the factions with denominator 13, there are **12 fractions** from $\frac{1}{13}$ to $\frac{12}{13}$.
But the decimal for $\frac{1}{13}$ has only **6 figures**, and so can only supply 6 of the 12 possible decimals from $\frac{1}{13}$ to $\frac{12}{13}$.
This is why $\frac{2}{13}$ has a different sequence of figures in its decimal to $\frac{1}{13}$.
$\frac{2}{13}$ supplies the other 6 possible decimals.
It is possible to obtain all the twelve decimals for the fractions from $\frac{1}{13}$ to $\frac{12}{13}$ from

the decimals for $\frac{1}{13}$ and $\frac{2}{13}$. You may like to see if you can do this.

RECIPROCALS

The **reciprocal** of a number is 1 divided by that number.

For example the reciprocal of 3 is $\frac{1}{3}$ which is $0.\dot{3}$

1 Copy out and complete the two centre columns of the table below showing the reciprocals of the numbers from 1 to 16. Three of the decimals have been put in for you. The others should be found by looking at the earlier examples and exercises or by doing the divisions.

Number	Reciprocal	Decimal Equivalent	Type
1	$\frac{1}{1}=$	1	
2	$\frac{1}{2}=$		
3	$\frac{1}{3}=$		
4			
5			
6			TR
7	$\frac{1}{7}=$	$0.\dot{1}4285\dot{7}$	R
8			T
9			
10	$\frac{1}{10}=$	0.1	
11			
12			
13			
14			
15			
16	$\frac{1}{16}=$		

These decimals (and all others) can now be classified as being one of three types:

T: those which terminate, like $\frac{1}{8}$.

R: those which recur, like $\frac{1}{3}$ and $\frac{1}{7}$.

TR: those which have a terminating part and a recurring part, like $\frac{1}{6} = 0.1\dot{6}$ (in which there is a 1 which does not recur and a 6 which does.
$\frac{1}{14}$ is also of this type.

2 Put T, R or TR in the right-hand column of your table, depending on which type it is.

You should have: 7 T-types,
5 R-types,
4 TR-types.

PRIME FACTORS

If the denominator of a fraction is written as a product of prime factors we can predict whether the decimal of a fraction is a T-type, an R-type or a TR-type.

The denominators of all T-type decimals have only the factors 2 and/or 5 in them (this is because our number system is based on the number 10 which is 2×5).

> In fact, in T-type decimals each 2, 5 or 10 contributes one non-recurring figure in the decimal.

for example since $4=2\times2$ there will be two non-recurring figures in the decimal, and since $8 = 2\times2\times2$ there are three non-recurring figures: check with your table.

> Denominators containing factors of 3, 7, 11 or higher primes (or products of these), but no 2's or 5's are R-types: they recur, either with a single figure or in a block.

For example $\frac{1}{3}, \frac{1}{7}, \frac{1}{21}, \frac{1}{77}$ are R-types.

> Denominators which have 2's and/or 5's **and** 3, 7, 11 or higher primes as factors are always TR-types, with both a terminating part and a recurring part.

For example $12 = 2\times2\times3$, so its reciprocal will have two terminating figures (because of the 2×2) and a recurring figure (because of the 3).

❋ Look at your table again and check that the above facts are true for these 16 fractions.

EXAMPLE 12

For $\frac{7}{24}$ (the numerator is not relevant), since $24 = 2\times2\times2\times3$ we will expect its decimal to be three figures followed by a recurring part. We can write TTTR.

EXAMPLE 13

And for $\frac{11}{42}$ since $42 = 2\times3\times7$ there will be a single figure (indicated by the 2) followed by a recurring part.
This is a TR decimal.

These rules assume that the fraction is in its lowest terms.

EXAMPLE 14

For $\frac{22}{60}$ we first cancel down to $\frac{11}{30}$ and seeing a factor of 10 in the denominator (we ignore the factors of 2 and 5 if we see a factor of 10) we can predict a single terminating figure followed by a recurring part.

This is also a TR decimal.

EXERCISE 6

For each of the fractions below find how many terminating figures there are in the decimal and whether it has a recurring part as well:

a $\frac{5}{18}$ **b** $\frac{9}{26}$ **c** $\frac{2}{33}$ **d** $\frac{29}{56}$ **e** $\frac{59}{60}$

f $\frac{1}{72}$ **g** $\frac{3}{32}$ **h** $\frac{16}{69}$ **i** $\frac{27}{46}$ **j** $\frac{3}{88}$

k $\frac{20}{34}$ (remember to cancel here) **l** $\frac{16}{150}$

The 9 point circle diagram at the beginning of each chapter of this book is the pattern for one divided by the chapter number. So for Chapter 7, for example, the recurring decimal pattern for $\frac{1}{7}$ is shown. Non-recurring decimals like $\frac{1}{5} = 0.2$ are considered to have zero recurring at the end: $0.2\dot{0}$.

"God created the integers, the rest is the work of man."

Leopold Kronecker (1823–91)

GERMAN MATHEMATICIAN

"The only natural objects of mathematical thought are the integers."

Henri Poincaré (1854–1912)

FRENCH MATHEMATICIAN

6

THE ARITHMETIC OF BAR NUMBERS

We have studied whole, or natural numbers so far.
We now expand our number system to include **integers**, which are numbers that have a sign: plus or minus.

You will remember that we use bar numbers when we write, for example, $38 = 4\bar{2}$.

In this chapter we see how to add, subtract, multiply and divide bar numbers (also called negative numbers or minus numbers).

ADDITION AND SUBTRACTION

In fact we have already seen numbers like this when we solve a problem like the following.

EXAMPLE 1

If the temperature is 5° and it falls by 7° what is the new temperature?

It would clearly be 2 degrees below zero, which we call minus 2, or –2, or $\bar{2}$.

We can write this as: $5 - 7 = -2$ or $\bar{2}$.

In this kind of arithmetic every number is plus or minus. If a number has no minus sign before it or above it, then it is plus.

You may find a **number line** like the one below helpful with these sums.
Make a copy in your book.

$\bar{7}\quad \bar{6}\quad \bar{5}\quad \bar{4}\quad \bar{3}\quad \bar{2}\quad \bar{1}\quad 0\quad 1\quad 2\quad 3\quad 4\quad 5\quad 6\quad 7$

The Sutra in use here is the *Sankalana* Sutra: *By Addition and By Subtraction.*

EXAMPLE 2

$\bar{7} - 4 = \overline{11}$

Starting at $\bar{7}$ we go down (left on the number line) 4 units and arrive at $\overline{11}$.

EXAMPLE 3

$\bar{8} + 6 = \bar{2}$ From $\bar{8}$ we go 6 units to the right, arriving at $\bar{2}$.

EXAMPLE 4

$\bar{7} + 9 = 2$ From $\bar{7}$ we go up 9 units to 2.

EXERCISE 1

Find:

a $3 - 9$ **b** $7 - 11$ **c** $4 - 15$ **d** $18 - 27$ **e** $\bar{6} - 9$ **f** $\bar{7} + 5$

g $\bar{8} + 10$ **h** $3 - 12$ **i** $\overline{11} - 17$ **j** $\overline{12} + 4$ **k** $\overline{12} + 15$ **l** $\overline{13} + 6$

☺ BAR NUMBERS GAME

for 2, 3 or 4 players.

- Each player has a board and 3 "men" and 12 cards are dealt to each player.
- Aim: to get the 3 men at START onto the squares marked 16.
- The player can look at the cards. Some are blue (plus) cards, some are red (minus) cards.
- The player to the left of the dealer lays a card of their choice and moves a piece forward by that amount. Only one piece can be moved at a time.
- When the next player lays their card it is always combined with the previous card's value. So if the first card was 15, and then $\overline{7}$ is laid, that player must move forward 8.
- So every player combines the card they lay with the one showing and moves forwards or backwards, depending on the total: for $\overline{7}$ and 2, go back 5,
  for $\overline{3}$ and $\overline{5}$ go back 8,
  and so on.
- If you go beyond 27 you get to START, but you cannot go beyond START, whether going forwards or backwards: you must restart that piece.
- The game ends when all the cards have been laid.
- The winner is the first player to get their 3 men onto 16. If this is not achieved the winner is the player whose men are closest to 16 at the end.

EXAMPLE 5

We can also use the number line to add and subtract bar numbers: imagine a person who can walk along the number line. he can face in either direction and he can also walk forwards or backwards. Given $7 + \overline{6}$ for example, we start at 7 and let the minus on the 6 tell us to face in the minus direction (to the left), and let the sign (+) between the numbers tell us that the person is walking forwards.

So we start at 7 and go 6 steps to the left, arriving at 1: $7 + \overline{6} = 1$.

The first number tells us where to start.
The last number will be either positive or negative and tells us which way to face.
And we are either adding or subtracting these numbers:
for adding we walk forwards
for subtracting we walk backwards.

EXAMPLE 6

$4 - \bar{5} = 9$

Here we start at 4, face the left, and step 5 units backwards. In this case we find that we actually go to the right and arrive at 9.
We can summarise this method as follows:

forwards or backwards direction to face

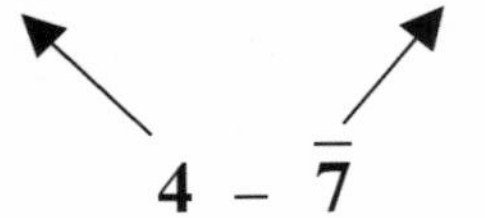

$$4 - \bar{7}$$

EXERCISE 2

Find:

a $2 + \bar{4}$ **b** $3 + \bar{1}$ **c** $\bar{5} + \bar{2}$ **d** $8 + \bar{5}$ **e** $6 - \bar{2}$ **f** $\bar{4} - \bar{3}$

g $\bar{5} - \bar{7}$ **h** $10 - \overline{12}$ **i** $17 + \overline{17}$ **j** $22 + \bar{1}$ **k** $\overline{18} - \bar{5}$ **l** $3 - 4.2$

m $5 - 6\frac{1}{2}$ **n** $\overline{10} + \overline{3.3}$

EXAMPLE 7

$3 \times \bar{4} = \overline{12}$

This is because $3 \times \bar{4}$ means $\bar{4}$ three times, or $\bar{4} + \bar{4} + \bar{4}$, which is $\overline{12}$.

EXERCISE 3

Find:

a $11 - 20$ **b** $\bar{7} + 15$ **c** $8 + \overline{11}$ **d** $\bar{9} + \bar{3}$ **e** $7 \times \bar{4}$ **f** $5 - \bar{8}$

g $\bar{6} - \overline{10}$ **h** $-7 - \bar{7}$ **i** $-19 + 9$ **j** $0 \times \bar{9}$ **k** $8 - \bar{8}$ **l** $5 \times \bar{3}$

APPLICATIONS IN ALGEBRA

We have seen how we can simplify various types of algebraic expressions.
For example $3a + 20b + 2(4a - 3b) = 3a + 20b + 8a - 6b = 11a + 14b$.
Check that you agree with this answer.

Now however we can tackle cases where bar numbers come in.

EXAMPLE 8

Simplify $3x + 5y - x - 7y$.

For the x terms: $3x - x = 2x$ and for the y terms: $5y - 7y = -2y$.
So the answer is $\underline{2x - 2y}$.

EXAMPLE 9

Find the value of $10 - x$ when $x = \overline{6}$.

$10 - x = 10 - \overline{6} = 16$.

EXERCISE 4

Simplify the following:

a $8a - 11a$ **b** $4x - 5x$ **c** $9x + 5y - 3x - 7y$ **d** $3x - 4y - 5x - 6y$

e $-7x + y - 3x + 8y$ **f** $5x - 6x + 7x$ **g** $3x - 6z - 3x + 3z$

h $2(3x + 4y) + 3(x - 3y)$ **i** $8(3a - 5b) - 30a - 30b$ **j** $x + 4(2x - 9y) + y$

k $2(a + b - c) + a - 5b$

If $x = \overline{3}$ find the value of: **l** $20 + x$ **m** $x - 15$ **n** $33 - x$ **o** $-x - 8$

MULTIPLICATION AND DIVISION

We can interpret the multiplication sum: $2 \times \overline{3}$ (which is a plus number multiplied by a minus number) as meaning **do twice: subtracting 3** (i.e. subtract 3 twice).

Subtracting 3 twice means subtracting 6, so $\mathbf{2 \times \overline{3} = \overline{6}}$

Next consider the case of multiplying a minus by a plus number.
We interpret $\overline{2} \times 3$ as meaning **do the opposite twice: adding 3**.

The opposite of adding 3 is subtracting 3, so we conclude that $\mathbf{\overline{2} \times 3 = \overline{6}}$

Next take $\overline{2} \times \overline{3}$ which must mean **do the opposite twice: subtracting 3**.
This is the same as adding 6, so $\mathbf{\overline{2} \times \overline{3} = 6}$

Finally the easiest case is 2×3 which means **do twice: add 3**, which means add 6.
So $\mathbf{2 \times 3 = 6}$.

Summarising these four results:

> If the signs of the numbers being multiplied are the same the answer is plus: e.g. $3 \times 5 = 15$,
> $\overline{3} \times \overline{5} = 15$.
>
> If the signs are opposite the answer is minus: $3 \times \overline{5} = \overline{15}$,
> $\overline{3} \times 5 = \overline{15}$.

These same rules also apply to division with bar numbers.

Since $2 \times \overline{3} = \overline{6}$ dividing both sides of this equation by 2 we get $\overline{3} = \frac{\overline{6}}{2}$ which shows that a minus number divided by a plus number gives a minus number.

Since also $\bar{2} \times \bar{3} = 6$ dividing both sides by $\bar{2}$ gives $\bar{3} = \frac{6}{\bar{2}}$ showing that a plus divided by a minus is also a minus.

Next we can divide both sides of $2 \times \bar{3} = \bar{6}$ by $\bar{3}$ we get $2 = \frac{\bar{6}}{\bar{3}}$ showing that a minus divided by a minus gives a plus, just as a plus divided by a plus gives a plus.

> For multiplication and division of bar numbers:
> Like signs give a plus,
> Opposite signs give a minus.

EXAMPLE 10

If $x = \bar{3}$ find the value of **a** $5x$ **b** $-7x$ **c** $\bar{2}x$ **d** $10 - 2x$.

a $5x = 5 \times \bar{3} = \overline{15}$ **b** $-7x = -7 \times \bar{3} = 21$ **c** $\bar{2}x = \bar{2} \times \bar{3} = 6$

d $10 - 2x = 10 - \bar{6} = 10 + 6 = 16$

EXERCISE 5

If $x = 5$ and $y = \bar{4}$ find the value of:

a $3y$ **b** $-6y$ **c** $\overline{15}y$ **d** xy **e** $-7x$ **f** $6 + 3y$

g $x - 2y$ **h** $5x + y$ **i** $-x - y$ **j** $y - 2x$ **k** $x + y - 1$

BRACKETS

EXAMPLE 11

Multiply out the brackets in **a** $-3(2a - 9b)$ **b** $6 - (4x - 2)$.

a $-3(2a - 9b) = -6a + 27b$ because $-3 \times 2 = -6$ and $-3 \times -9 = +27$. ☞

b 6 – (4x – 2) = 6 – 4x + 2 = 8 – 4x here there is no number in front of the bracket, but we can suppose that there is a 1 there:
6 – (4x – 2) = 6 – 1(4x – 2)

EXERCISE 6

Multiply out the brackets and simplify where possible:

a –5(6x – 4y) **b** –8(9a + 8b) **c** –3(16a – b +53c)

d $\bar{6}$ (14p – 15q) **e** –4(58x + 28) **f** –34(36t – 20)

g 4(2x – 3y) – 9(x – 5y) **h** 5(ab + 7) – 3(5ab + 10)

i –4(a + 2b + 1) – (6a – b + 1)

NIKHILAM MULTIPLICATION AGAIN

You will recall the easy way to multiply numbers which are near to a base number, or a multiple of a base number.

EXERCISE 7

Multiply the following mentally:

a 94 × 97 **b** 88 × 95 **c** 98 × 98 **d** 89 × 89

e 104 × 109 **f** 123 × 104 **g** 1021 × 1003 **h** 888 × 997

i 987 × 995 **j** 303 × 306 **k** 71 × 72 **l** 197 × 196

So far all the examples have been where the numbers are both above or both below the base, or a multiple of the base.

EXAMPLE 12

Find 124 × 98.

Here one number is over and the other is under 100:
The differences from 100 are +24 and –2.
Crosswise gives 122 (124–2 or 98+24).

$$\begin{array}{r} 124 + 24 \\ \underline{98 - 2} \\ \underline{122 / \overline{48}} \end{array} = \underline{\mathbf{12152}}$$

So 122 is the left-hand part of the answer.
Then multiplying the differences we get –48, written $\overline{48}$ (since a plus times a minus gives a minus). This gives the answer as $122\overline{48}$.

To remove the negative portion of the answer we just take 48 from one of the hundreds in the hundreds column. This simply means reducing the hundreds column by 1 and applying **All From 9 and the Last From 10** to 48.
Thus 122 becomes 121 and $\overline{48}$ becomes 52.
So $124 \times 98 = 122\overline{48} = \underline{12152}$

EXAMPLE 13

$1003 \times 987 = 990/\overline{039} = \underline{989/961}$

Similarly, we first get 1003 – 13 = 990 or 987 + 3 = 990,
and +3 × –13 = $\overline{039}$ (three figures required here as the base is 1000).

Then 990 is reduced by 1 to 989, and applying the formula to 039 gives 961.

So these sums are just like the others except that we need to clear the minus part at the end.

EXAMPLE 14

$121 \times 91 = 11\overset{\bar{1}}{2}/\overline{89} = \underline{110/11}$.

Here we have a minus one to carry over to the left so that the 112 is reduced by 2 altogether.

EXERCISE 8

Find:

a 104 × 91	**b** 94 × 109	**c** 103 × 98	**d** 92 × 112
e 91 × 111	**f** 106 × 89	**g** 91 × 103	**h** 91 × 107
i 91 × 105	**j** 991 × 1005	**k** 987 × 1006	**l** 992 × 1111

"When he was fifteen Johann Dase gave demonstrations of his amazing talents. He could multiply together mentally 'two 8-figure numbers in 54 seconds, two 20-figure numbers in 6 minutes, two 40-figure numbers in 40 minutes and two100-figure numbers in 8 hours."

7

GENERAL MULTPLICATION

We have seen various methods of multiplication but they were all for special cases, where some special condition was satisfied, like both numbers being close to 100 for example.
We come now to the general multiplication technique, by which any two numbers can be multiplied together in one line, by mere mental arithmetic.
First let us briefly revise how we multiply by a single figure number.

EXAMPLE 1

Find 74 × 8.

We multiply each of the figures in 74 by 8 starting on the left:

7 × 8 = **56** and 4 × 8 = **32**.

These are combined by carrying the 3 in 32 over to the 6 in 56: 5 6,3 2 = 592.

The inner figures are merged together. So 74 × 8 = 592.

EXAMPLE 2

Find 827 × 3.

The three products are **24**, **6**, **21**.

The first two products are combined: 24,6 = 246 no carry here as 6 is a single figure,
then 246 is combined with the 21: 246,21= 2481. So 827 × 3 = 2481.

EXAMPLE 3

Find 77 × 4.

The products are **28**, **28**.

And 28,28 = 308 (the 28 is increased by 2 to 30). So 77 × 4 = 308.

EXERCISE 1

Multiply the following mentally:

a 73 × 3 **b** 63 × 7 **c** 424 × 4 **d** 777 × 3

e 654 × 3 **f** 717 × 8 **g** 876 × 7

EXAMPLE 4

Find 21 × 23.

Think of the numbers set out one below the other:

```
 2  1
 2  3 ×
 4 8 3
```

There are 3 steps:

A. multiply vertically in the left-hand column: 2 × 2 = **4**, so 4 is the first figure of the answer.

```
 2  1
 |
 2  3 ×
 4
```

☞

B. multiply crosswise and add:
$2 \times 3 = 6$,
$1 \times 2 = 2$, $6 + 2 = \mathbf{8}$,
so 8 is the middle figure of the answer.

```
2   1
  ×
2   3 ×
4 8
```

C. multiply vertically in the right-hand column: $1 \times 3 = \mathbf{3}$,
3 is the last figure of the answer.

```
2   1
    |
2   3 ×
4 8 3
```

EXAMPLE 5

Find 14 × 21.

```
1   4
2   1 ×
2 9 4
```

A: vertically on the left: $1 \times 2 = \mathbf{2}$,
B: crosswise: $1 \times 1 = 1$, $4 \times 2 = 8$ and $1 + 8 = \mathbf{9}$,
C: vertically on the right: $4 \times 1 = \mathbf{4}$.

This is of course very easy and straightforward, and we should now practice this vertical and crosswise pattern to establish the method.

EXERCISE 2

Multiply mentally:

a 22 31 ×	**b** 21 31 ×	**c** 21 22 ×	**d** 22 13 ×
e 61 31 ×	**f** 32 21 ×	**g** 31 31 ×	**h** 13 13 ×

The previous examples involved no carry figures, so let us consider this next.

EXAMPLE 6

Find 23 × 41.

```
  2  3
  4  1  ×
  9 4 3
```

The 3 steps give us: 2 × 4 = **8**,
2 × 1 + 3 × 4 = **14**,
3 × 1 = **3**.

The 14 here involves a carry figure, so in building up the answer mentally from the left we merge these numbers as before.

The mental steps are: 8
8,14 = 94 (the 1 is carried over to the left)
94,3 = 943

So 23 × 41 = <u>943</u>.

EXAMPLE 7

Find 23 × 34.

```
  2  3
  3  4  ×
  7 8 2
```

The steps are: 6
6,17 = 77
77,12 = <u>782</u>

EXAMPLE 8

Find 33 × 44.

```
   3  3
   4  4
 1 4 5 2
```

The steps are: 12
12,24 = 144
144,12 = <u>1452</u>

We can now multiply any two 2-figure numbers together in one line.
This is clearly an application of the *Vertically and Crosswise* Sutra.

EXERCISE 3

Multiply the following mentally:

a	21	47
b	23	43
c	24	29
d	22	28
e	22	53
f	31	36
g	22	56
h	31	72
i	44	53
j	33	84
k	33	69
l	34	42
m	33	34
n	22	52
o	34	66
p	51	54
q	35	67
r	55	59
s	54	64
t	55	63
u	44	81
v	45	81
w	48	72
x	34	19
y	38	88

z Can you see how this method simplifies when
- **i** both numbers end in a 1,
- **ii** the last figures of the numbers, or the first figures, or both figures of one number, are the same?

You may have found in this exercise that you prefer to start with the crosswise multiplications, and put the left and right vertical multiplications on afterwards.

Explanation

It is easy to understand how this method works.
The vertical product on the right multiplies units by units and so gives the number of units in the answer. The crosswise operation multiplies tens by units and units by tens and so gives the number of tens in the answer. And the vertical product on the left multiplies tens by tens and gives the number of hundreds in the answer.

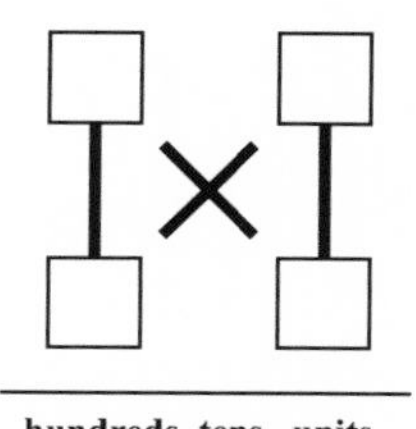

MULTIPLYING 3-FIGURE NUMBERS

EXAMPLE 9

Find 123 × 132.

```
   1 2 3
   1 3 2 ×
 1 6 2 3 6
```

The *Vertically and Crosswise* formula can be extended to deal with this, but in fact the usual vertical/crosswise/vertical pattern can be used on this sum also.

We can split the numbers up into 12/3 and 13/2, treating the 12 and 13 as if they were single figures:

```
 12    3
 13    2
162  3 6
```

vertically	12 × 13 = **156**,
crosswise	12 × 2 + 3 × 13 = **63**,
vertically	3 × 2 = **6**.

Combining these mentally we get: 156
156,63 = 1623
1623,6 = 16236

EXERCISE 4

Multiply, treating the numbers as 2-figure numbers:

a 112 × 203 **b** 123 × 131 **c** 123 × 122 **d** 112 × 123 **e** 421 × 22

EXAMPLE 10

304 × 412 = 125248

Here we may decide to split the numbers after the first figure: 3/04 × 4/12.

```
 3    04
 4    12
12 52 48
```

When we split the numbers in this way the answer appears **two digits at a time**.

☞

The 3 steps of the pattern are: $3\times4 = \mathbf{12}$,
$3\times12 + 4\times4 = \mathbf{52}$,
$4\times12 = \mathbf{48}$.

These give the 3 pairs of figures in the answer.

EXERCISE 5

Multiply using pairs of digits:

a 2 1 1 3 0 4	**b** 3 0 7 4 0 7	**c** 2 0 3 4 3 2	**d** 2 1 1 3 1 1
e 5 0 4 5 0 4	**f** 5 0 1 5 0 1	**g** 7 1 2 1 1 2	**h** 7 0 3 2 1 1

MOVING MULTIPLIER

In multiplying a long number by a single figure, for example 4321 × 2, we multiply each of the figures in the long number by the single figure. We may think of the 2 moving along the row, multiplying each figure vertically by 2 as it goes.

EXAMPLE 11

THE MOVING MULTIPLIER

Find 4321 × 32.

4 3 2 1
3 2

Similarly here we put 32 first of all at the extreme left.
Then vertically on the left, $4 \times 3 = \mathbf{12}$.
And crosswise, $4\times2 + 3\times3 = \mathbf{17}$.

4 3 2 1
  3 2

Then move the 32 along and multiply crosswise:
$3\times2 + 2\times3 = \mathbf{12}$.

4 3 2 1
    3 2

Moving the 32 once again:
multiply crosswise, $2\times2 + 1\times3 = \mathbf{7}$.
Finally the vertical product on the right is $1\times2 = \mathbf{2}$. ☞

These 5 results (in bold), 12,17,12,7,2 are combined mentally, as they are obtained, in the usual way:

12,17 = 137

137,12 = 1382

1382,7,2 = <u>138272</u>

So we multiply crosswise in every position, but we multiply vertically also at the very beginning and at the very end.

EXAMPLE 12

31013 × 21

Here the 21 takes the positions:

```
31013      31013      31013      31013
21          21          21          21
```

The 6 mental steps give: 6,5,1,2,7,3
so the answer is <u>651273</u>.

EXERCISE 6

Multiply using the moving multiplier method:

a 3 2 1 × 2 1

b 3 2 1 × 2 3

c 4 2 1 × 2 2

d 3 2 1 × 4 1

e 1 2 1 2 × 2 1

f 1 3 3 1 × 2 2

g 1 3 1 3 × 3 1

h 1 1 2 2 1 × 2 2

i Write down your answers to the above sums to 2 significant figures.

WRITTEN CALCULATIONS

It is also useful to be able to write out our multiplications.
In the Vedic system we can do this from left to right or from right to left.
Here we use the right to left method, but the formula is the same: *Vertically and Crosswise*.

EXAMPLE 13

Find 42 × 31.

The sum is set out as before:

A. We **multiply vertically on the right**: 2×1 = **2**,
and put this down as the right-hand figure of the answer.

B. Then we **multiply crosswise** and add to get 4+6 = **10**.
So we put down 0 and carry 1 to the left.

$$\begin{array}{rrrr} & & 4 & 2 \\ & & 3 & 1 \\ \hline 1 & 3 & 0 & 2 \\ \hline & _1 & & \end{array}$$

C. Finally we **multiply vertically on the left**: 4×3 = **12**,
12 + the carried 1 makes 13, which we put down.

EXAMPLE 14

Find 86 × 23.

A. The method is as above: vertically on the right, 6×3 = **18**,
put down 8 carry 1.

B. Crosswise, 24 + 12 = **36**, 36 + carried 1 = 37,
put down 7 carry 3.

$$\begin{array}{rrrr} & & 8 & 6 \\ & & 2 & 3 \\ \hline 1 & 9 & 7 & 8 \\ \hline & _3 & _1 & \end{array}$$

C. Vertically on the left, 8×2 = **16**, 16 + carried 3 = 19,
put down 19.

EXAMPLE 15

Find 4321 × 24.

Here we can use the moving multiplier method.

A. First, vertically on the right, 1×4 = 4, put it down.

B. Crosswise, 8 + 2 = 10, put down 0, carry 1.

☞

C. Next we cross-multiply the 32 with the 24, this gives 12+4 = 16, 16 + carried 1 gives 17, put down 7 carry 1.

```
    4 3 2 1
        2 4
1 0 3 7 0 4
  2 1 1
```

D. Then cross-multiply the 43 with the 24, this gives 16+6 = 22, 22 + carried 1 gives 23, put down 3 carry 2.

E. Vertically on the left, 4×2 = 8, 8 + carried 2 gives 10, put down 10.

Imagine the 24 in the three positions if you can, rather than writing it down three times.

EXERCISE 7

Multiply the following from right to left:

a 31 × 41	**b** 23 × 22	**c** 61 × 42	**d** 52 × 53
e 54 × 45	**f** 78 × 33	**g** 17 × 71	**h** 88 × 88
i 231 × 32	**j** 416 × 41	**k** 182 × 23	**l** 473 × 37
m 5432 × 32	**n** 6014 × 24	**o** 3333 × 22	**p** 44444 × 33

"The chief aim of all investigations of the external world should be to discover the rational order and harmony which has been imposed on it by God and which he revealed to us in the language of mathematics."

Johannes Kepler (1571–1630)

GERMAN ASTRONOMER

ALGEBRAIC MULTIPLICATION

In this chapter we see how the algebraic notation develops to deal with algebraic multiplications, and how the numerical methods of the previous chapter can be applied in algebra,

MULTIPLYING AND DIVIDING SINGLE TERMS

It is important to remember that sometimes the number one is implied and not written.
For example **where we write x we mean 1x**.

Also **x means x^1** though the ^{1} is not usually written.

EXAMPLE 1

Find **a** $a^2 \times a^3$ **b** $b^5 \div b^2$ ☞

a Since $a^2 = a{\times}a$ and $a^3 = a{\times}a{\times}a$ then $a^2 \times a^3 = a \times a \times a \times a \times a = \underline{a^5}$.

b $b^5 \div b^2 = \frac{b \times b \times b \times b \times b}{b \times b} = \underline{b^3}$ since two b's cancel from the top and bottom.

These examples show that:

for multiplication we add the powers, and for division we subtract the powers.
Algebraically we can write: $a^m \times a^n = a^{m+n}$ and $a^m \div a^n = a^{m-n}$.

The Sutra here is *Sankalana Vyavakalanabhya: By Addition and By Subtraction.*

EXERCISE 1

Find:

a $a^3 \times a^5$ **b** $c \times c^3$ **c** $p^4 \times p^{10}$ **d** $a^2 \times a^4 \times a^3$ **e** $s^{15} \times s^{17}$ **f** $y \times y$

g $z^5 \times z \times z^2$ **h** $h^{29} \times h^{29}$ **i** $i^8 \div i^3$ **j** $j^7 \div j^2$ **k** $k^{50} \div k^{17}$ **l** $1^{100} \div 1$

Next we bring in the *Anurupyena* Sutra, *Proportionately.*

EXAMPLE 2

Find **a** $3x^4 \times 5x^3$ **b** $18x^6 \div 3x^2$ **c** $7x^4 \div x$.

a $3x^4 \times 5x^3 = \underline{15x^7}$ the powers are added but the coefficients are multiplied.

b $18x^6 \div 3x^2 = \underline{6x^4}$ the powers are subtracted and the coefficients are divided.

c remember $x = 1x^1$ so $7x^4 \div x = \underline{7x^3}$.

EXERCISE 2

Find:

a $5a^3 \times 3a^7$ **b** $2b^8 \times 6b^9$ **c** $c^4 \times 5c^3$ **d** $5d^5 \times 2d$

e $10e^7 \div 2e^2$ **f** $18f^9 \div 3f^5$ **g** $8g^5 \div 2g$ **h** $27h^4 \div h^3$

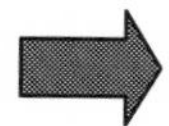

EXAMPLE 3

Find **a** $2a^2b \times 3a^5b^2$ **b** $9x^2y^5 \div 3xy$.

a $2a^2b \times 3a^5b^2 = \underline{6a^7b^3}$ we multiply the coefficients to get 6, add the powers on **a** to get a^7, add the powers on **b** to get b^3. N.B. $\mathbf{b = b^1}$.

b $9x^2y^3 \div 3xy = \underline{3xy^2}$ divide the coefficients (9÷3=3), subtract the powers on x and on y.

EXERCISE 3

Find:

a $x^3 \times x^2$ **b** $3x^7 \times 7x^2$ **c** $6y^3 \times y^8$ **d** $y^2 \times y^3 \times y^4$

e $x^{21} \times x$ **f** $6x \times 7x$ **g** $x \times 2x^2 \times 3x^3$ **h** $p \times p^2$

i $x^2y^3 \times x^5y^6$ **j** $2x^3y^5 \times 6xy^2$ **k** $5a^2b \times 8a^3b^2$ **l** $3ab \times 6a^2$

m $2a \times 3b \times 4ab$ **n** $8x^5 \div 2x^2$ **o** $42x^5 \div 6x^3$ **p** $18x^8 \div 6x$

q $x^9 \div x$ **r** $8x^5y^{11} \div 2xy^3$ **s** $6a^3b^4c^2 \div 2ab^2c$ **t** $2x^5 \div x^3$

u $12x^7 \div 4x^2$ **v** $10a^5b^5 \div 2ab^2$ **w** $3w^3 \div w^3$

Of particular significance for some later work is the result that any number raised to the power of zero is equal to 1: $3^0 = 1$, $1.7^0 = 1$, $x^0 = 1$ etc.

This can be demonstrated as follows.
$3^2 \div 3^2 = 1$ because we are dividing a number, 9, by itself (9÷9=1).
But subtracting the powers as in the last exercise we get $3^2 \div 3^2 = 3^0$.
Therefore $\mathbf{3^0 = 1}$.

Similarly $x^1 \div x^1 = 1$ by division and $x^1 \div x^1 = x^0$ by subtracting the powers. So $\mathbf{x^0 = 1}$.

MULTIPLYING BINOMIALS

An expression with two terms is called a **binomial**. E.g. 2x – 3.

EXAMPLE 4

Multiply 3x(5x – 7).

We have to multiply each of the terms of the binomial (5x–7) by 3x.
So $3x(5x - 7) = \underline{15x^2 - 21x}$.

Similarly, $2x(3x + 4y) = \underline{6x^2 + 8xy}$.

EXERCISE 4

Multiply the following:

a 2x(3x + 4) **b** 5x(x – 9) **c** x(18x + 19) **d** 7y(4y – 15) **e** 3x(5x – 4y)

EXAMPLE 5

Multiply: (x + 3)(x + 4).

We have to multiply x+3 by x+4.
This means that the x and the 3 in x+3 must both multiply the x and the 4 in x+4.

The best way to do this is to use the *Vertically and Crosswise* method. ☞

Put one binomial under the other:
Multiply vertically on the left: $x \times x = x^2$.
Cross-multiply and add: $4 \times x + 3 \times x = 7x$.
Multiply vertically on the right: $3 \times 4 = 12$.

$$\begin{array}{ll} x & +\ 3 \\ \underline{x} & \underline{+\ 4} \\ \hline x^2 + 7x + 12 & \end{array}$$

It is just like multiplying two 2-figure numbers together.
Multiply from left to right or right to left: whichever you like.

EXERCISE 5

Multiply:

a $(x + 5)(x + 6)$ **b** $(x + 2)(x + 9)$ **c** $(x + 10)(x + 1)$ **d** $(x + 20)(x + 20)$

e $(x + 1)(x + 1)$ **f** $(x + 22)(x + 28)$ **g** $(y + 52)(y + 4)$ **h** $(x + 4)^2$

EXAMPLE 6

Multiply $(2x + 5)(3x + 2)$.

$$\begin{array}{ll} 2x & +\ 5 \\ 3x & +\ 2 \\ \hline 6x^2 + 19x + 10 & \end{array}$$

Vertically on the left: $2x \times 3x = 6x^2$.
Crosswise: $4x + 15x = 19x$.
Vertically on the right: $5 \times 2 = 10$.

EXAMPLE 7

Multiply $(x + 3y)(5x + 7y)$.

$$\begin{array}{ll} x & +\ 3y \\ 5x & +\ 7y \\ \hline 5x^2 + 22xy + 21y^2 & \end{array}$$

On the left: $x \times 5x = 5x^2$.
Crosswise: $7xy + 15xy = 22xy$.
On the right: $3y \times 7y = 21y^2$.

EXERCISE 6

Multiply the following: ☞

a $(2x + 5)(x + 4)$ **b** $(x + 8)(3x + 11)$ **c** $(2x + 1)(2x + 20)$ **d** $(2x + 3)(3x + 7)$

e $(4x + 3)(x + 6)$ **f** $(3x + 17)(3x + 4)$ **g** $(6x + 1)(5x + 1)$

h $(2x + 5)(4x + 5)$ **i** $(3x + 3)(4x + 5)$ **j** $(2x + 3y)(2x + 5y)$

k $(5x + 2y)(2x + 5y)$ **l** $(4x + 3y)(7x + y)$ **m** $(7x + y)(x + 7y)$

n $(x + y)(x + y)$

Next we need to use the methods for combining negative numbers.

EXAMPLE 8

Multiply $(2x - 3)(3x + 4)$.

This is very similar:
$2x \times 3x = 6x^2$,
Crosswise: $8x - 9x = -1x$ or $-x$.
And $-3 \times 4 = -12$.

$$\begin{array}{lr} 2x & -\ 3 \\ \underline{3x} & \underline{+\ 4} \\ \underline{6x^2} & \underline{-\ x\ -\ 12} \end{array}$$

EXAMPLE 9

Find $(x - 3)(x - 6)$.

Vertically: $x \times x = x^2$,
Crosswise: $-6x - 3x = -9x$,
Vertically: $-3 \times -6 = +18$.

$$\begin{array}{lr} x & -\ 3 \\ \underline{x} & \underline{-\ 6} \\ \underline{x^2 - 9x + 18} & \end{array}$$

EXERCISE 7

Multiply:

a $(x + 3)(x - 5)$ **b** $(x + 7)(x - 2)$ **d** $(x - 4)(x + 5)$ **d** $(x - 5)(x - 4)$

e $(x - 3)(x - 3)$ **f** $(2x - 3)(x + 4)$ **g** $(2x - 3)(3x + 6)$ **h** $(3x - 1)(x + 7)$

i $(4x + 3)(2x - 5)$ **j** $(x + 5)(4x - 7)$ **k** $(x + 1)(9x - 1)$ **l** $(2x + 1)(2x - 1)$

There may be more than one letter in the sum:

EXAMPLE 10

Multiply (x – y)(2x – 3y).

$x \times 2x = 2x^2$,
crosswise: $-3xy - 2xy = -5xy$,
$-y \times -3y = +3y^2$.

$$\begin{array}{ll} x & -\ y \\ \underline{2x} & \underline{-\ 3y} \\ \underline{2x^2 - 5xy + 3y^2} \end{array}$$

EXAMPLE 11

Multiply (a + b)(c + d).

$$\begin{array}{ccc} a & + & b \\ \underline{c} & \underline{+} & \underline{d} \\ \underline{ac\ +\ ad} & \underline{+\ bc} & \underline{+\ bd} \end{array}$$

EXERCISE 8

Multiply:

a (3x + 4y)(2x – 3y) **b** (6x + y)(2x – 5y) **c** (x + 2y)(2x – y)

d (3x – 4y)(2x + 3y) **e** (3x – 4y)(2x – 3y) **f** (4x – 5y)(4x + 5y)

g 2x(3x – 4y) **h** 6x(x + 8y) **i** a(b + c)

FACTORISING QUADRATIC EXPRESSIONS

The reverse process is also important.
We need to be able, given an expression like $2x^2 - 6x$, to write it as a product.

EXAMPLE 12

Factorise $2x^2 - 6x$.

In the two terms here we see a common factor of 2 and also a common factor of x.
We can therefore take out 2x as a factor and write: $2x^2 - 6x = \underline{2x(x - 3)}$. ☞

We can check that this is correct by multiplying out $2x(x-3)$ to get $2x^2 - 6x$.

Similarly, given $3x^2 - 6$, only 3 is a common factor so $3x^2 - 6 = \underline{3(x^2 - 2)}$.

EXERCISE 9

Factorise the following:

a $12x^2 + 9x$	**b** $8x^2 - 10x$	**c** $4x^2 - 7x$	**d** $x^2 + 9x$	**e** $10x^2 + 15x$
f $10x^2 + 15$	**g** $9y^2 - 5y$	**h** $g^2 + 19g$	**i** $2x^2 - x$	**j** $6x^2 + 9x$
k $6x^2 + 8x$	**l** $6x^2 + 8$	**m** $6x^2 + 7x$	**n** $6x^2 - 6x$	**o** $6x^2 - 6$

Factorising quadratic expressions consisting of three terms will be dealt with later.

*"Ten-year old Truman Henry Safford was asked: Multiply in your head 365,365,365,365,365,365 by 365,365,365,365,365,365.
He flew around the room like a top, pulled his pantaloons over the top of his boots, bit his hand, rolled his eyes in their sockets, sometimes smiling and talking,and then seeming to be in an agony, until, in not more than one minute, said he, 133,491,850,208,566,925,016,658,299,941,583,225!'"*

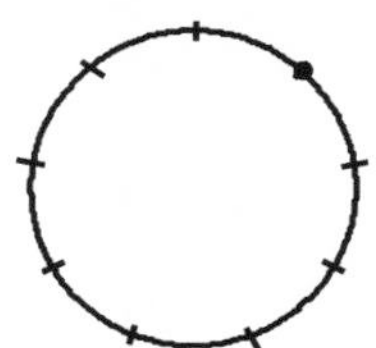

SQUARING

The *Vertically and Crosswise* formula simplifies nicely when the numbers being multiplied are the same, and gives us a very easy method for squaring numbers.

THE DUPLEX

We will use the term **Duplex**, D, as follows:

for 1 figure **D is its square**, e.g. $D(4) = 4^2 = \mathbf{16}$;

for 2 figures **D is twice their product**, e.g. $D(43) = 2\times4\times3 = \mathbf{24}$;

EXERCISE 1

Find the Duplex of the following numbers:

a 5 **b** 23 **c** 55 **d** 2 **e** 14 **f** 77 **g** 26 **h** 90

> The square of any number is just the total of its Duplexes, combined in the way we have been using for mental multiplication.

EXAMPLE 1

$43^2 = \underline{1849}$

Working from left to right there are three duplexes in 43:D(4), D(43) and D(3).

D(4) = **16**, D(43) = **24**, D(3) = **9**,

combining these three results in the usual way we get:

16
16,24 = 184
184,9 = 1849

EXAMPLE 2

$64^2 = \underline{4096}$

D(6) = **36**, D(64) = **48**, D(4) = **16**,

So mentally we get:

36
36,48 = 408
408,16 = 4096

EXERCISE 2

Square the following:

a 31	**b** 14	**c** 41	**d** 26	**e** 23	**f** 32	**g** 21
h 66	**i** 81	**j** 91	**k** 56	**l** 63	**m** 77	**n** 33

NUMBER SPLITTING

You may recall that we could sometimes group two figures as one when we were multiplying two 2-figure numbers together. This also applies to squaring.

EXAMPLE 3

$123^2 = \underline{15129}$

Here we may think of 123 as 12/3, as if it were a 2-figure number:

D(12) = 12^2 = **144**,
D(12/3) = 2 × 12 × 3 = **72**,
D(3) = 3^2 = **9**.

Combining these: 144,72 = 1512, and 1512,9 = $\underline{15129}$

EXERCISE 3

Square the following, grouping the first pair of figures together:

a 121 **b** 104 **c** 203 **d** 113 **e** 116 **f** 108 **g** 111

EXAMPLE 4

$312^2 = \underline{97344}$

Here we can split the number into 3/12 but we must work with **pairs of digits**:

D(3) = **9**, D(3/12) = **72**, D(12) = **144**.

Combining: 9,72 = 972 we can put both figures of 72 after the 9,
972,144 = 97344

EXERCISE 4

Square the following, grouping the last two figures together:

a 211 **b** 412 **c** 304 **d** 902 **e** 407 **f** 222 **g** 711

ALGEBRAIC SQUARING

Exactly the same method gives us squares of algebraic expressions.

EXAMPLE 5

Find $(x + 5)^2$.

This is just like squaring numbers: we find the duplexes of x, x+5 and 5.

$D(x) = \mathbf{x^2}$, $D(x+5) = 2\times x\times 5 = \mathbf{10x}$, $D(5) = 5^2 = \mathbf{25}$.

So $(x + 5)^2 = \underline{x^2 + 10x + 25}$.

EXAMPLE 6

Find $(2x + 3)^2$.

There are three Duplexes: $D(2x) = \mathbf{4x^2}$, $D(2x+3) = 2\times 2x\times 3 = \mathbf{12x}$, $D(3) = \mathbf{9}$.

So $(2x + 3)^2 = \underline{4x^2 + 12x + 9}$.

EXAMPLE 7

Find $(x - 3y)^2$.

Similarly: $D(x) = \mathbf{x^2}$, $D(x-3y) = 2\times x\times -3y = \mathbf{-6xy}$, $D(-3y) = \mathbf{9y^2}$.

So $(x - 3y)^2 = \underline{x^2 - 6xy + 9y^2}$.

EXERCISE 5

Square the following:

a $(3x + 4)$	**b** $(5y + 2)$	**c** $(2x - 1)$	**d** $(x + 7)$
e $(x - 5)$	**f** $(x + 2y)$	**g** $(3x + 5y)$	**h** $(2a + b)$
i $(2x - 3y)$	**j** $(x + y)$	**k** $(x - y)$	**l** $(x - 8y)$

☺ **SQUARES GAME** for 2, 3,4 or 5 players.

1) You will need a pack of cards. Everyone has a piece of paper with their name on it and a pen. From the pack select all those numbered 1 to 6 (ace counts as 1) and one 7, one 8 and one 9. This makes 27 cards. One player is chosen to keep scores.

2) Shuffle the cards and deal out 5 cards to each player (players can look at their cards), followed by two cards which are placed beside each other to form a 2-figure number.

3) Everyone mentally finds the square of this number and writes the answer down on their paper which they put face down in the centre of the table until everyone's paper is in a pile on the table. Once an answer is in the pile it cannot be altered. Then everyone with the correct answer gets a point but the person who wrote the first correct answer (nearest to the bottom of the pile) gets two points.

4) The person to the left of the dealer then selects one of his/her five cards and puts it on top of the left of the two cards on the table. This forms another 2-figure number and (3) above is repeated. The game continues with the next player placing a card on the right pile, and so on, placing the cards alternately. When all the cards are used the player with the highest score is the winner.

Number Splitting

THE MOEBIUS STRIP

❋ Take a sheet of graph paper and cut a strip longways 2cm wide.

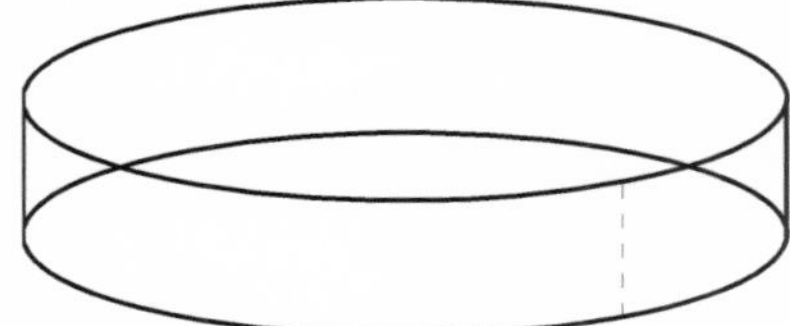

If the strip was glued as shown to form a loop it would have 2 separate edges and 2 faces (one inside and one outside).

❋ Make a loop with your strip but before gluing the ends together **give one end a half turn**.
This is a Moebius Strip, named after a mathematician who studied its properties.

1 Near one edge of your strip write the letter A on both sides of the strip. Write B near the opposite edge and on both sides.

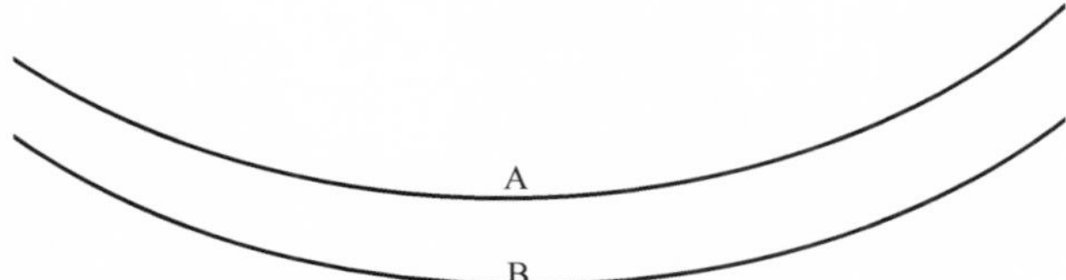

Follow the edge marked A around until you return to A. What do you find?

2 Now draw a line along the middle of your strip until you return to the point you started at. Examine the line and write down what you find.

The Moebius Strip has only one edge and only one side.

3 Using scissors cut the strip along the line you have just drawn. Write down what you get from this. Is the result another Moebius Strip?

4 Cut another strip from your graph sheet but this time it should be 3cm wide.
Make another Moebius Strip.

Cut along the strip again but this time cut 1cm from one side:

cut

Describe carefully what you get.

❋ Try some variations of your own.
You could try putting 2 or 3 half-twists into the strip instead of just one and you could examine the number of edges and faces or cut the strip in half or in thirds.

Another interesting idea is to cut out a cross shape like the one below and glue all 4 ends together to form 2 perpendicular loops. You can put a twist in one or both of the loops and cut in half to see what happens.

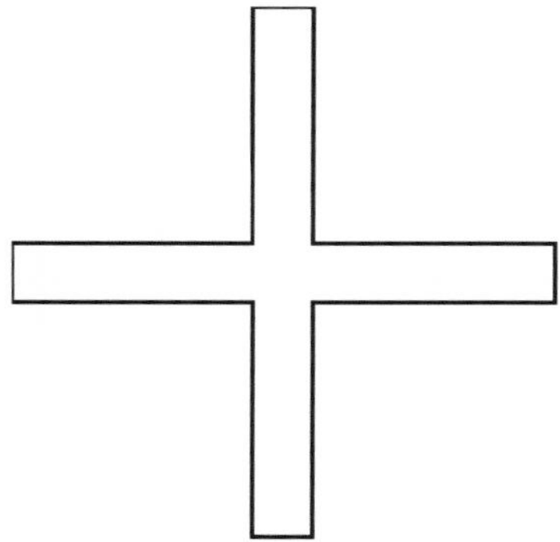

"That vast book which stands forever open before our eyes, the universe, cannot be read until we have learned the language and become familiar with the characters in which it is written. It is written in mathematical language, without which means it is humanly impossible to comprehend a single word.

Galileo Galilei (1564–1642)

ITALIAN SCIENTIST

10

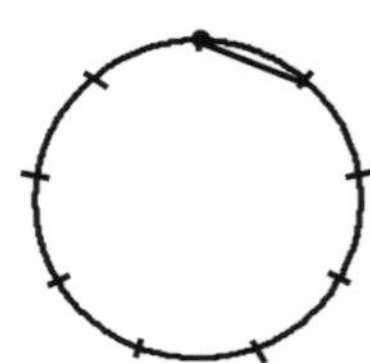

SEQUENCES

In this chapter, we will be looking at some simple number sequences and generating formulae for these patterns.
Some of these sequences can be built up using simple geometric shapes and patterns.
We are going to start with the pattern below.

1 Make the shapes shown below with matchsticks and then fill in the table below, by extending the pattern.

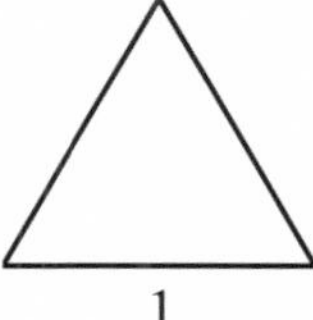

1

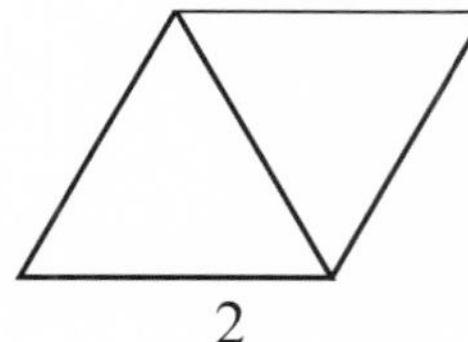

2

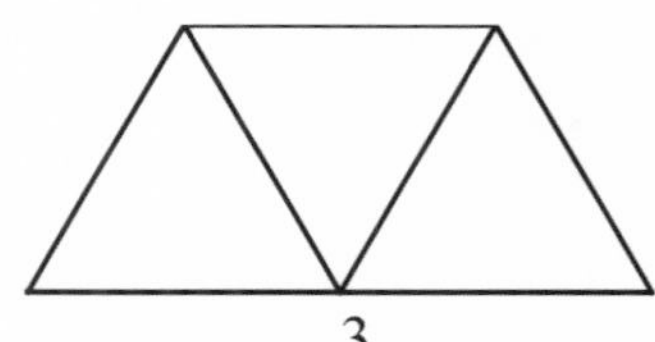

3

Number of shape	1	2	3	4	5	6
Number of matchsticks	3					

The Sutras in use in this chapter are *By One More than the One Before* and *By Mere Observation.*

Be careful not to confuse this pattern with the triangular number sequence in Chapter 6 of Book 1. You may need to look back at that chapter to see the difference. This is a sequence that happens to be generated out of triangles!
You have seen sequences like this before and you have had practice finding the **next** one or two terms. In Chapter 6 of Book 1 you were asked to find the 30th term.

❋ Check that you agree the next term in the table above would be 15 and the 30th term 61.

This is all very well, but when you get on to high numbers like this, it is a little awkward to have to count all the way through every possible number until you arrive at the one you want. What would you do if you wanted the 86th term? It would be much more convenient to have a general formula into which we could substitute the number we wanted, say the 7th, 20th or even 50th term and produce the answer straight away. This is exactly what we are going to try and do, by producing what is usually called **a formula for the nth term**.

THE Nth TERM

Now look at the basic sequence: **1, 2, 3, 4, 5, 6 . . . .**

This sequence, which goes up by 1 each time, is special because each number gives the **position** of that number: **3** is in the **3rd** place, **7** is in the **7th** place. And **n** is in the **nth** place.

This is very simple but it means that we can describe other sequences in terms of **n** using this basic sequence.

For example, in the sequence **2 , 4 , 6 , 8 , 10 , 12 , 14 . . . .**
the numbers are all double those in the basic sequence **1, 2, 3, 4, 5, 6, 7 . . .**
The numbers also go up by 2 each time:

2 , 4 , 6 , 8 , 10 , 12 , 14 . . . .

+2 +2 +2 +2 +2 +2

This gives us a very important clue as to the general formula or nth term.
This means the **nth term** for this sequence is given by the formula **2n**.

The following sequence goes up by 3 each time and each number is 3 times the basic sequence
1, 2, 3, 4, 5, 6, 7 . . .

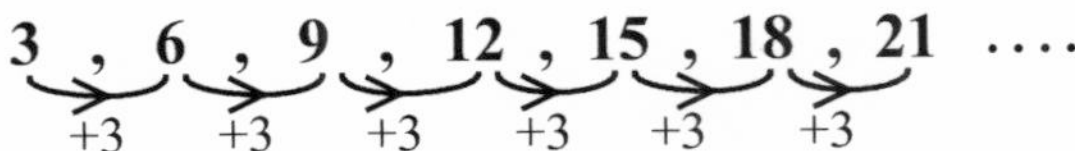

The **nth term** here would be given by **3n**.

2 What do you think the nth term is for the following sequence?
5 , 10 , 15 , 20 , 25 , 30....

3 What do you think the nth term is for the following sequence?
6 , 12 , 18 , 24 , 30 , 36....

4 What do you think the nth term is for the following sequence?
12 , 24 , 36 , 48 , 60 , 72....

Now let us return to the sequence in your table: **3 , 5 , 7 , 9 , 11 , 13 , 15.....**

We notice that the sequence goes up by 2 each time, so the formula will be similar to **2n**. What is the difference between this sequence and the one for which the nth term is 2n (2,4,6,8,10,12,14.....)?

The numbers are all one more than in this sequence. so the nth term here is **2n+1.**

We can also check that we can produce the correct sequence from the formula as follows, using the formula **2n+1**:

If n=1, 2n+1 = **3**,
if n=2, 2n+1 = **5**,
if n=3, 2n+1 = **7**,
if n=4, 2n+1 = **9**,
if n=5, 2n+1 = **11** etc.

This is exactly the sequence we started with. We can also relate this to our original pattern with equilateral triangles. For each additional triangle we made we needed to add two extra matchsticks, except for the first one where we started with three (one more than two). This original triangle or base triangle is then always there, no matter how many extra triangles we add. This equates clearly with the formula **2n+1**.

EXAMPLE 1

Find the nth term for the following sequence:

8 , 11 , 14 ,17 , 20 , 23....

The increase each time is 3, so the formula will contain **3n**.
But **3n** generates **3, 6, 9, 12, 15 . . . .** and in the sequence above each number is **5 more** than this.
So the formula will be **3n+5**.

Check: putting n=1,2,3,4,5... into this formula gives us the given series: 8,11,14,17,20.....

The method of finding the nth term of a sequence that increases by a regular amount each time is summarised below.

a) First determine the amount you go up by each time. This will tell you whether it is 2n, 3n, 4n etc. For example, if it increases by 5 each time it will be 5n.
b) Look at the first term of the given sequence. If it is more than the amount by which the sequence increases, add the extra amount to your n term.
If the first term is less than the amount by which the sequence increases, subtract from your n term as shown in the next example.
c) Check that you can generate the sequence you require from your formula.

EXAMPLE 2

Find the nth term for the following sequence:

1 , 8 , 15 , 22 , 29 , 36....

The formula starts with 7n, as it increases by 7 each time.
We started at 1 not 7. 1 is 6 below 7, so the formula must be **7n–6**
Putting n=1,2,3,4,5... into 7n-6 gives us 1,8,15,22,29....

5 Use matches to make the following shapes and draw a table similar to that on page 78. Then generate a formula for the nth term. Check you can generate the sequence from your formula.

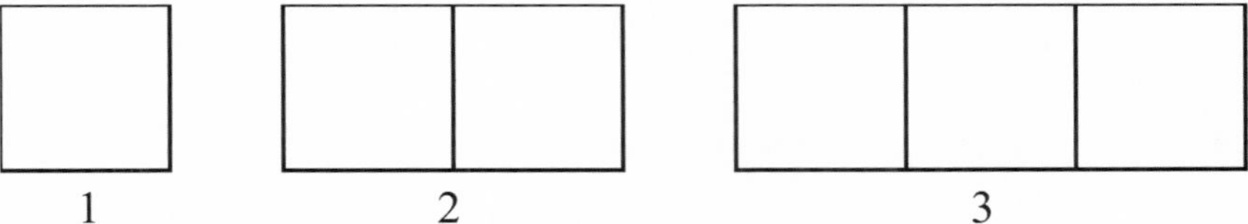

6 Do the same thing for the following pattern as you did for question 4.

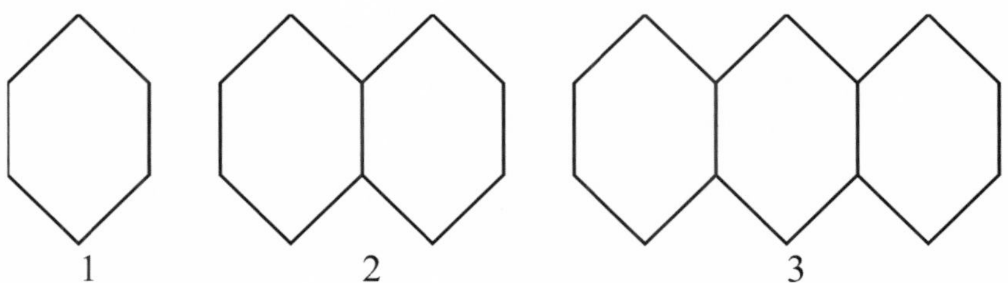

7 This time continue the following pattern in your book, make a table and find a formula.
Check your formula.

EXERCISE 1

Find a formula for the nth term of the following sequences. Check your formulae mentally.

a 8,16,24,32,40,48.....
b 10,20,30,40,50,60.....
c 1,2,3,4,5.6.....
d 3,4,5,6,7,8....
e 5,7,9,11,13,15...
f 2,5,8,11,14,17.....
g 12,18,24,30,36,42.....
h 15,20,25,30,35,40.....
i 2,7,12,17,22,27.....
j 3,12,21,30,39,48.....
k 0,4,8,12,16,20
l 72,75,78,81,84,87.....

EXERCISE 2

Go back to Exercise 1 and by using the formulae you have found write down the 30th, 60th and 87th term in each sequence.

SEQUENCES INVOLVING FRACTIONS

EXAMPLE 3

It may be that we want to find the formula for a series involving fractions.

$$\frac{1}{2}, \frac{1}{3}, \frac{1}{4}, \frac{1}{5}, \frac{1}{6} \ldots$$

Here it is best to consider the numerator and denominator separately. The numerator does not really have a formula, it is always 1. The formula for the denominator is n+1. So the nth term would be given by $\frac{1}{n+1}$.

EXAMPLE 4

What is the nth term of the following sequence?

$$\frac{3}{2}, \frac{5}{6}, \frac{7}{10}, \frac{9}{14}, \frac{11}{18} \ldots$$

The formula for the numerator is 2n+1 and the formula for the denominator is 4n–2. So the nth term would be $\frac{2n+1}{4n-2}$.

EXERCISE 3

Find formulae for the following sequences. Again check your answers mentally.

a $\frac{1}{1}, \frac{1}{2}, \frac{1}{3}, \frac{1}{4}, \frac{1}{5} \ldots$ **b** $\frac{1}{4}, \frac{1}{8}, \frac{1}{12}, \frac{1}{16}, \frac{1}{20} \ldots$ **c** $\frac{1}{1}, \frac{1}{4}, \frac{1}{7}, \frac{1}{10}, \frac{1}{13} \ldots$

d $\frac{1}{2}, \frac{2}{3}, \frac{3}{4}, \frac{4}{5}, \frac{5}{6} \ldots$ **e** $\frac{1}{6}, \frac{2}{11}, \frac{3}{16}, \frac{4}{21}, \frac{5}{26} \ldots$ **f** $\frac{3}{4}, \frac{6}{8}, \frac{9}{12}, \frac{12}{16}, \frac{15}{20} \ldots$

g $\frac{2}{3}, \frac{5}{5}, \frac{8}{7}, \frac{11}{9}, \frac{14}{11} \ldots$ **h** $\frac{1}{1}, \frac{2}{2}, \frac{3}{3}, \frac{4}{4}, \frac{5}{5} \ldots$

8 What does the last sequence in part **h** simplify to?

"We see .... that the theory of probabilities is at the bottom only common sense reduced to calculation; it makes us appreciate with exactitude what reasonable minds feel by a sort of instinct, often without being able to account for it"

Marquis de Pierre Simon Laplace (1749–1827)

FRENCH MATHEMATICIAN

11

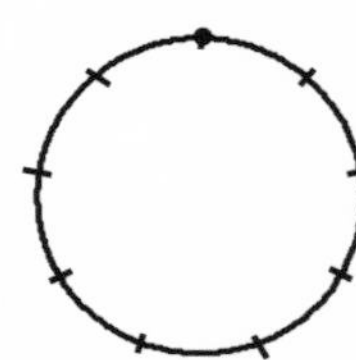

PROBABILITY

CERTAIN, UNCERTAIN AND IMPOSSIBLE

Some things are certain to happen, for example it is certain that the number following an even number will be odd.

Some things are impossible, for example finding a triangle with four sides.
These are two extremes and in between are things that may or may not happen. For example, it may or it may not rain tomorrow.

impossible ________________________________ certain

This line shows the range of possibilities, from impossible to certain.
Where, on this line, would you put the possibility of rain tomorrow?

EXERCISE 1

For each of the following decide how likely they are, and put the letters a,b,c ....j on a copy of the above line, where you think they should go:

a Half the class will be away tomorrow.

b It will snow here in December.

c It will snow here in April.

d It will snow here in August.

e The next car you see will be red.

f It will rain here this week.

g You will meet your favourite pop star today.

h It will be exactly 4 o'clock when you get home.

i The next person you meet will have a name beginning with J.

j If you toss a coin it will be heads.

☺ **PROBABILITY GAME** for 2 to 8 players.

You will need the board, a counter for each player, a coin and a dice.
About half the players are in the coins team and half in the dice team.
The coins team start with their counters at one end of the board and the dice team at the other end. Each player chooses a lane.
The aim is for one team to get all their counters to the other end before the other team.
Toss the coin to decide which team starts, then take turns: the coins team always tossing their coin and the dice team always throwing their dice.
Each player in the coins team moves their counters forward 6 places if it is a head and 3 places if it is a tail.
The dice team move forward by the number shown on the dice.
Play the game at least four times.

1 Are the coins team or the dice team more likely to win?

2 How can you find out which team has the better chance of winning?

3 How could you change the scores for heads and tails so that each team has an equal chance of winning?

SCALE OF PROBABILITIES

It is usual for the scale of probabilities to go from 0 to 1.

0____1
impossible certain

So impossible events have a probability of 0.
And certain events have a probability of 1.
All other events have a probability value between 0 and 1.
And events which are equally likely to happen or not happen have a probability of ½ or 0.5 (sometimes called "evens").

4 Go back to the list in Exercise 1 and give a value (between 0 and 1) for each event.
If the answer is not obvious describe what you could do, or what you would need to know, to get some idea of the answer.

POSSIBLE OUTCOMES

It is often useful when studying probabilities to know what the possible outcomes of an event are.
For example the possible outcomes of a football match are win, lose, draw: 3 possibilities.

For a person's star sign there are 12 possibilities: Aries, Gemini etc.

EXERCISE 2

For each of the following give the number of possible outcomes:

a a coin is tossed

b a die is thrown

c the first letter of someone's name

d the day of the week of someone's birthday

☞

e the day of the year of someone's birthday

f the first letter of the month of someone's birthday

5 We said there are three possibilities for the outcome of a football match: win, lose or draw.
Do you think the probabilities for these are $\frac{1}{3}$, $\frac{1}{3}$ and $\frac{1}{3}$? If not, why not?

6 How could you estimate the probabilities for a particular football team?

7 How could you estimate the probability of rain next May 1st?

EXAMPLE 1

The outcome of the last 12 matches of a particular football team is known to be:

W W L D W L L W D W W L where W=win, L=lose and D=draw.

Use this information to estimate what is most likely and least likely to happen in their next match, and find out the probabilities for win, lose and draw.

We can begin by counting up how many times they have won, lost and drawn:

there are 6 wins,
4 matches lost
and 2 drawn.

Clearly **winning is most likely and drawing is least likely in the next match**, based on the last 12 matches.

As they have won 6 times out of 12 the probability of winning will be $\frac{6}{12}$ or $\frac{1}{2}$.
Similarly they lost 4 times so the probability of losing is $\frac{4}{12} = \frac{1}{3}$.
And 2 draws means a probability of $\frac{2}{12} = \frac{1}{6}$.

The probability of an event is given by a fraction:

$$\text{Probability} = \frac{\text{number of times the event has happened}}{\text{maximum number of times it could have happened}}$$

EXERCISE 3

a The outcome of the previous 10 matches for a team are: L D W L L D D W L W. Find the probability of a win, lose and draw. What is the most likely outcome of the next match, based on this information?

b You have the following information about another team (team B) who are going to play team A above: D W L L D W W L L L.
Find the probabilities for team B. Which team do you think is more likely to win the match?

c The following information is available about teams X and Y who are going to play each other:
Team X: W L W W D W W L L W W D
Team Y: W D W W L W
Find the probabilities of win, lose and draw for both teams and decide who is favourite to win.

d Make a list of other factors that may need to be considered before deciding (e.g. players who are injured).

If you were not given the information about the football teams above you might have to find it yourself or find some other way of choosing between them (for example you could ask a number of people what they thought would happen).
If you need to know the probability of a car being red you could try to find out how many red cars there are and how many of other colours.

This could involve you in a survey to find out the numbers of different colours of car passing a particular place at a particular time. The probabilities could then be found from this information.

But there is another way of finding probabilities which does not rely on previous results or a survey.

THEORETICAL PROBABILITIES

If we toss a fair coin we know that we have 1 chance in 2 of getting heads so the probability of getting heads is $\frac{1}{2}$.

EXAMPLE 2

Find the probability of getting a 5 when throwing a fair dice.

There are 6 possible outcomes and only 1 of them is a 5, so the probability is 1 in 6 or $\frac{1}{6}$.

EXAMPLE 3

Find the probability of getting an odd number when throwing a fair dice.

There are 3 possibilities: 1, 3 or 5 so the probability is $\frac{3}{6} = \frac{1}{2}$.

Theoretical probability is given by a fraction:

$$\text{Probability} = \frac{\text{number of ways in which an event can occur}}{\text{total number of possible outcomes}}$$

Find the probability of picking a vowel out of a bag containing all the letters of the alphabet.

There are 26 letters altogether and 5 of them are vowels, so the probability is $\frac{5}{26}$.

EXERCISE 4

Find the probability of (cancel fractions where possible):

a getting 5 or 6 when throwing a fair dice

b picking the letter A from a bag containing all the vowels

c throwing a number less than 3 with a fair dice

d picking a club from a pack of cards

e picking an ace from a pack of cards

f getting a number below 7 when throwing a fair dice.

g 3 or less when two dice are thrown and the score is the total on the two dice.

"Let U = the University, G = Greek, and P = Professor, then GP = Greek Professor."

Lewis Carroll (1832–98)

ENGLISH MATHEMATICIAN AND AUTHOR

12

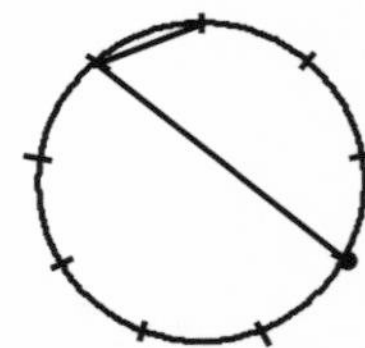

EQUATIONS

Another use of algebra is when we are given an equation which contains a letter, and we are asked to find the value that the letter represents.

ONE-STEP EQUATIONS

If, for example, we are given the equation **x + 5 = 8** we need to know what x can be so that when 5 is added to it, the total is 8.
This is clearly 3 because 3 + 5 = 8. So we say x=3.

EXAMPLE 1

Solve the equation 9 + x = 20.

Again it is not difficult to see that x=11, because 9+11=20.

You may have noticed in these two examples that you can get the answer by taking the number next to the x from the number on the other side of the equals sign.

EXAMPLE 2

Solve x + 39 = 70.

So to solve this equation we just take 39 from 70, so x=31.

EXAMPLE 3

Solve x – 7 = 8.

This says that when 7 is subtracted from a number we get 8.
What is the number?
We get x=15, since 15–7=8.

Notice again that we can get the answer easily, this time by adding the 7 to the 8.

EXAMPLE 4

Solve x – 13 = 30.

We find x = 43.

So for equations like **x + 6 = 7** or **6 + x = 7** we take the number on the left from the number on the right.

And for equations like **x – 6 = 7** we add the number on the left to the number on the right.

The Vedic Sutra operating here is *Paravartya Yojayet* which means *Transpose and Apply*.

Transpose means "reverse" and in solving equations *Transpose and Apply* means:

where something is **added** to the x-term: **subtract**,
where something is **subtracted** from the x-term: **add**.

EXERCISE 1

Solve the following equations, check each answer to make sure it is right:

a $x + 3 = 10$ **b** $x - 3 = 10$ **c** $x + 4 = 11$ **d** $20 + x = 100$ **e** $x - 6 = 2$

f $x - 15 = 7$ **g** $x - 19 = 44$ **h** $x + 88 = 100$ **i** $x - 3\frac{1}{2} = 4\frac{1}{2}$ **j** $x + 16 = 60$

k $x + 123 = 1000$ **l** $x - 18 = 18$ **m** $x + 1.3 = 5$

EXAMPLE 5

Solve $3x = 15$.

This says that 3 times a number is 15, so the answer is clearly 5, as 3 fives make 15.
So we write $\underline{x=5}$.

EXAMPLE 6

Solve $7x = 28$.

$\underline{x=4}$ (since 7 fours make 28).

Again you may notice that the easy way to get the answer is to divide the number on the right by the number on the left: $15÷3=5$ and $28÷7=4$.
So the *Transpose and Apply* formula is working here too: where x is **<u>multiplied</u>** by a number we **divide**. Divide is the opposite of multiply.

And if x is divided by a number we would expect to multiply:

EXAMPLE 7

Solve $\frac{x}{3} = 7$.

So x must be $3×7$. $\underline{x = 21}$

We can see this is right because $\frac{21}{3} = 7$.

EXAMPLE 8

$\frac{x}{23} = 30$. Since $23 \times 30 = 690$ we can say $x = \underline{690}$

EXERCISE 2

Solve the following, checking your answer each time.

a $3x = 21$ **b** $5x = 35$ **c** $2x = 26$ **d** $4x = 36$ **e** $6x = 54$

f $3x = 960$ **g** $2x = 76$ **h** $40x = 120$ **i** $3x = 333$ **j** $7x = 98$

k $2\frac{1}{2}x=10$ **l** $3\frac{1}{2}x=21$ **m** $\frac{x}{4}=5$ **n** $\frac{x}{3}=8$ **o** $\frac{x}{13}=3$

p $\frac{x}{3}=19$ **q** $2x=7$ **r** $\frac{x}{10}=40$ **s** $\frac{x}{60}=60$ **t** $6x=1800$

u $2x = 3.6$

TWO-STEP EQUATIONS

We have seen how the *Transpose and Apply* formula can be used in solving equations.
Sometimes two or more applications of the formula are needed, as the following examples show.

EXAMPLE 9

Solve $2x + 3 = 13$.

Can you see what x is here? A number is doubled and three is added and the result is 13.

You can first take 3 from both sides of the equation: this gives $2x = 10$.

Then you can see that $\underline{x = 5}$ is the answer. ☞

To check: $2\times\underline{5} + 3 = 13$ so it is correct.
There are two applications of *Transpose and Apply* here:
First the +3 indicates that we subtract 3 from 13 (to get 10),
then the 2x indicates that we divide 10 by 2.

 **EXAMPLE 10**

Solve $5x - 4 = 36$.

Using the Sutra we add 4 to 36 to get 40,
then $40 \div 5 = 8$, so $\underline{x = 8}$.

Check: $5\times 8 - 4 = 36$.

If you like you can write the sum out in steps like this:

$$5x - 4 = 36$$
$$5x = 40$$
$$\underline{x = 8}$$

But you should also be able to put the answer straight down.

 **EXAMPLE 11**

Solve $\frac{x}{7} + 3 = 5$.

Here we take 3 from 5 to get 2,
then multiply 2 by 7, so $\underline{x = 14}$

 **EXAMPLE 12**

Solve $\frac{2x}{3} = 4$.

Multiply 3 by 4 to get 12,
then $12\div 2=6$, so $\underline{x = 6}$

 **EXAMPLE 13**

Solve $\frac{x-3}{4} = 5$.

Because all the left side is divided by 4 we begin by multiplying 5 by 4,
then we add 3 to the result giving $\underline{x = 23}$

It is useful to think of a pair of scales when solving equations:

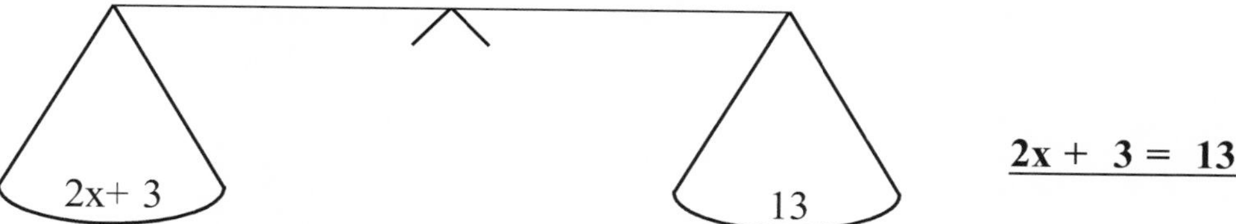

$2x + 3 = 13$

Because the two sides of the equation are equal, they balance.
And they will still balance if we add the same amount to each side, or subtract the same amount from each side:

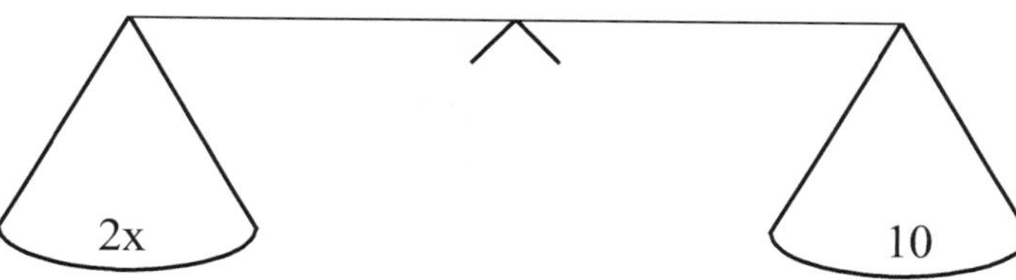

take 3 from both sides to get **$2x = 10$**

And they will still balance if we double each side, or multiply both sides by any number, or divide both sides by any number:

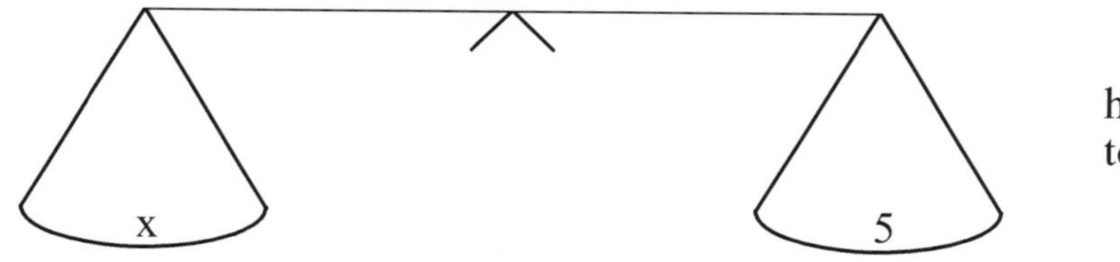

halve both sides to get **$x = 5$**

This is a very useful way of dealing with equations.

EXERCISE 3

Solve the following equations mentally. Check your answers.

a $3x + 7 = 19$ **b** $2x + 11 = 21$ **c** $3x + 5 = 29$ **d** $7x + 10 = 31$

e $4x - 5 = 7$ **f** $3x - 8 = 10$ **g** $5x - 21 = 4$ **h** $2x - 5 = 6$

i $\frac{x}{3} + 4 = 6$ **j** $\frac{x}{4} + 7 = 9$ **k** $\frac{x}{2} - 8 = 2$ **l** $\frac{x}{3} - 1 = 6$ ☞

m $\frac{2x}{3} = 8$ **n** $\frac{3x}{4} = 15$ **o** $\frac{5x}{3} = 15$ **p** $\frac{2x}{5} = 20$

q $\frac{x+4}{7} = 5$ **r** $\frac{x-21}{10} = 1$ **s** $2x + 1 = 3.8$ **t** $3x + 2 = 6.11$

THREE- STEP EQUATIONS

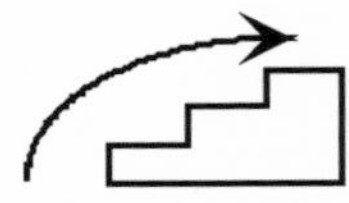

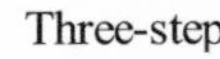

EXAMPLE 14

Solve $\frac{3x}{5} + 4 = 10$.

First $10 - 4 = 6$, then $6\times5 = 30$, then $30\div3 = 10$ so <u>$x = 10$</u>

EXAMPLE 15

Solve $\frac{3x+2}{4} = 8$.

First $8\times4 = 32$, then $32-2 = 30$, then $30\div3 = 10$ so <u>$x = 10$</u>

EXAMPLE 16

Solve $2(3x + 4) = 38$.

The bracket here indicates that 3x+4 is being multiplied by the number outside the bracket, which is 2.
So we begin by dividing 38 by 2.

First $38\div2 = 19$, then $19-4 = 15$, then $15\div3 = 5$ so <u>$x = 5$</u>

Alternatively, here, we can multiply the bracket out first:
If $2(3x + 4) = 38$ then $6x + 8 = 38$
and so $38-8 = 30$ and $30\div6 = \underline{5}$.

❋ Show that $x = 5$ is the solution to $2(3x + 4) = 38$.

EXERCISE 4

Solve the following:

a $\frac{2x}{3} + 4 = 8$ **b** $\frac{3x}{5} - 4 = 5$ **c** $\frac{7x}{2} - 10 = 11$ **d** $\frac{3x}{8} + 17 = 20$

e $\frac{2x+1}{3} = 4$ **f** $\frac{2x-3}{5} = 3$ **g** $\frac{5x+2}{3} = 9$ **h** $\frac{6x-1}{7} = 5$

i $3(5x - 2) = 54$ **j** $8(x + 3) = 64$ **k** $3(7x - 3) = 33$ **l** $2(4x + 3) = 102$

We sometimes have to work with bar numbers when solving equations as the next examples show.

EXAMPLE 17

Solve **a** $3x = \overline{15}$ **b** $-7x = \overline{56}$ **c** $\overline{2}x + 5 = 17$ **d** $3x + 11 = 2$.

a $x = \frac{\overline{15}}{3} = \overline{5}$ **b** $x = \frac{\overline{56}}{\overline{7}} = 8$ **c** $\overline{2}x = 12,\ x = \frac{12}{\overline{2}} = \overline{6}$

d $3x = 2 - 11,$
$3x = -9,$
$x = -3.$

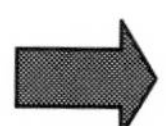

EXAMPLE 18

Solve $\overline{3}x = 24$.

We get $x = \frac{24}{\overline{3}}$ so $x = -8$ or $\overline{8}$.

EXERCISE 5

Solve:

a $5x = \overline{55}$

b $\overline{4}x = 48$

c $-3x = \overline{90}$

d $5x + 21 = 1$

e $8x - 2 = \overline{26}$

f $2x = \overline{7}$

g $3x = \overline{3.9}$

h $\overline{7}x - 3 = 4$

i $\overline{5}x = 20$

j $\overline{9}x = \overline{54}$

k $-3x - 7 = \overline{10}$

l $3x = \overline{6.6}$

m $2x = \overline{1.2}$

"Human subtlety . . . will never devise an invention more beautiful, more simple or more direct than does Nature, because in her inventions nothing is lacking, and nothing is superfluous."

Leonardo da Vinci (1452–1519)

ITALIAN PAINTER AND INVENTOR

13

ANGLES AND TRIANGLES

You may recall that a basic unit for measuring angles is the degree, and that there are 360 degrees, written 360° in a full circle.

So there are 180° in a half circle:

And 90° in a quarter circle, or right angle:

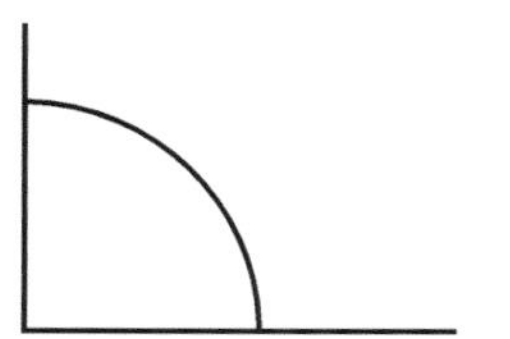

Angles can be measured and drawn with an instrument called a **protractor**. This has two scales one inside the other because angles can be measured clockwise or anti-clockwise.

MEASURING ANGLES

To measure an angle place the centre of the protractor, which is in the middle of the base line, on the corner, or vertex, of the angle. Then line up the base line with one side of the angle.

To measure the angle find the zero on the base line and measure round that scale to the other side of the angle and read off the number. There are always two ways of placing the protractor on the angle to read off the size.

The Sutra here is *Adyamadyenantyamantyena, The First by the First and the Last by the Last*.
This describes the way in which you line up one side of the angle with the base line and read off the answer on the other side of the angle.

EXERCISE 1

Measure the following angles to the nearest degree:

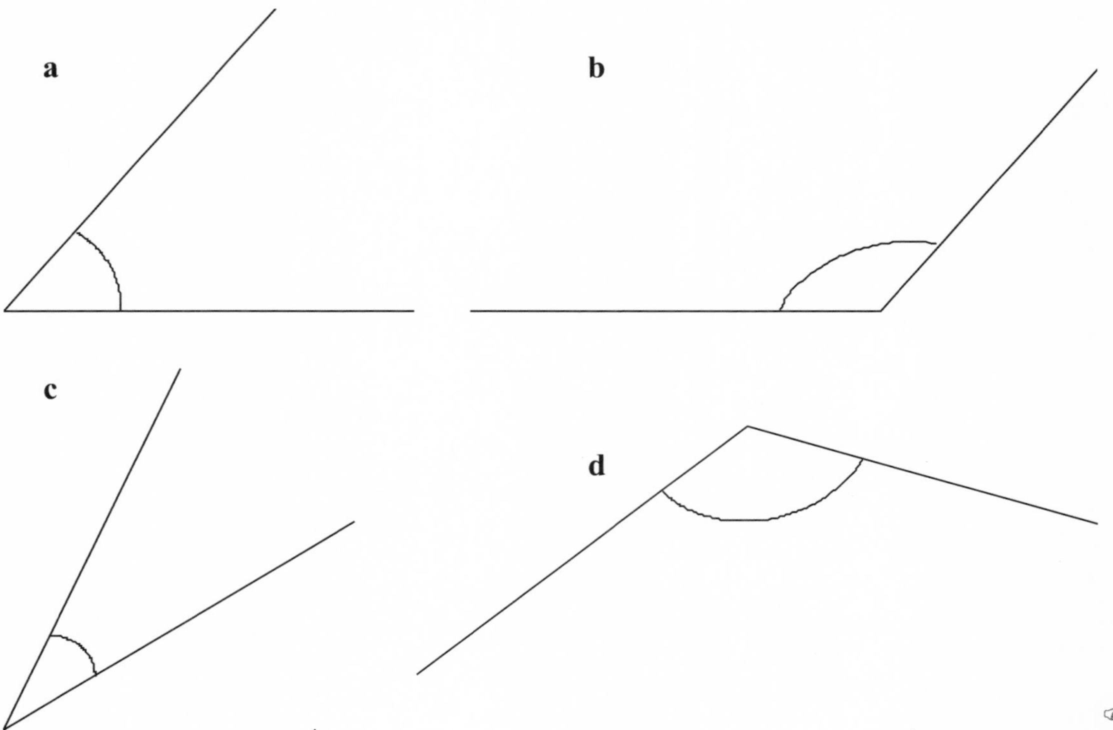

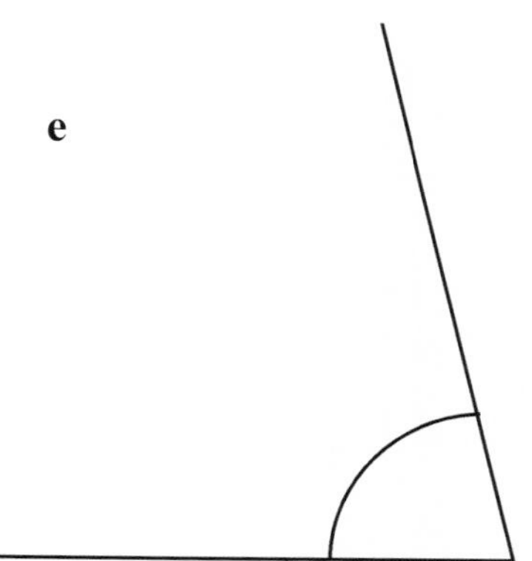

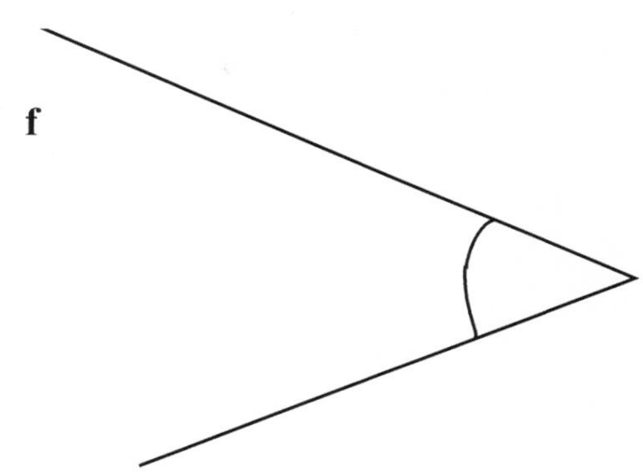

For angles greater than 180° (unless you have a circular protractor) we proceed as in the following example (using *By the Non-Completion*).

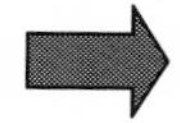

EXAMPLE 1

Find the angle A:

We measure angle B, which is 125°,

then 360° – 125° = 235°.

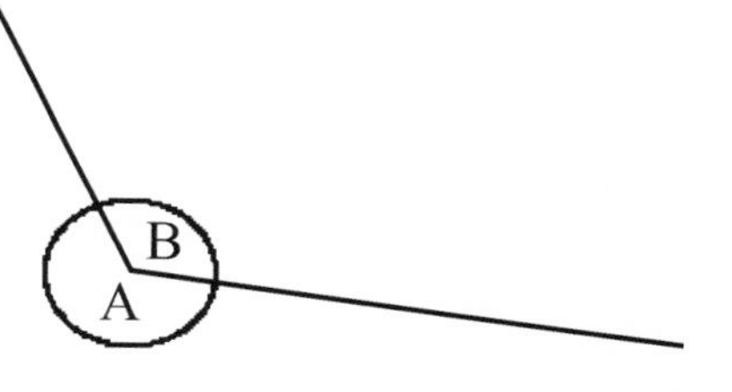

EXERCISE 2 Find the following angles:

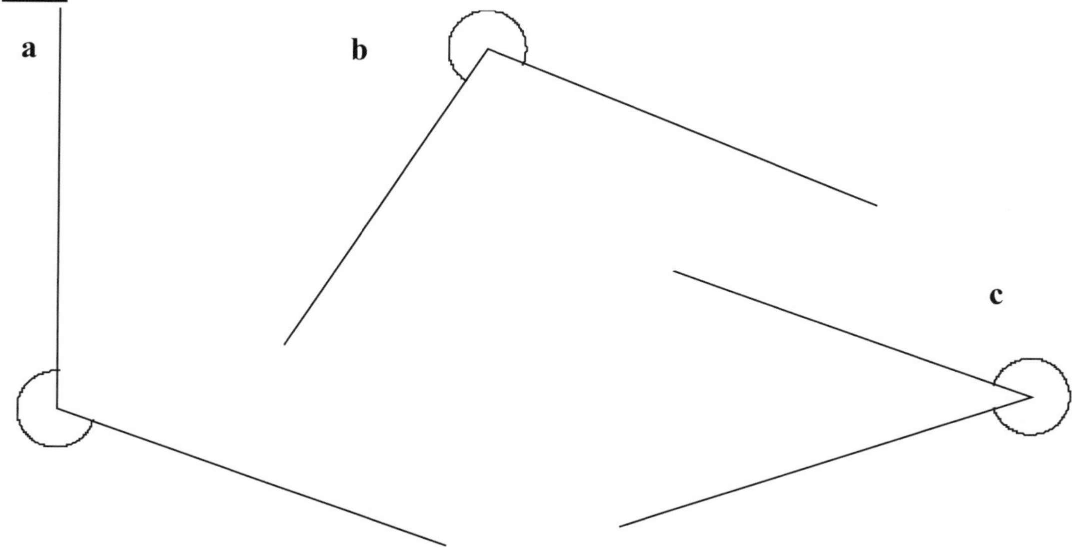

EXERCISE 3

To construct the mathematical curve called the **cardioid**.

a Measure the radius of your protractor and draw a circle on a sheet of plain paper with a radius 2mm more than this. Mark the centre of the circle clearly.

b Draw in the vertical diameter with your ruler and place your protractor with the base line on this diameter and with the centre of the protractor on the centre of the circle.

c Put a mark on the paper every 10° all the way around the circle.

d Number these points: start with the point at the bottom numbered 0 and number round the circle. When you get to 36 after going right round the circle put 36 below the 0 and continue numbering once more round the circle putting the numbers outside the first ones (you may number only the even numbers this time).

e Now, carefully, with ruler and sharp pencil join point 1 to point 2,
2 to 4,
3 to 6,
4 to 8 and so on until you get to 35.

You should in the end have a heart-shaped design called a **cardioid**.
This shape is often seen in a cup or bowl when a light shines into it. You may have seen it.
Write the name of the curve on your sheet.

DRAWING ANGLES

Next we consider the reverse process of using the protractor to draw an angle of a given size.

EXAMPLE 2

Draw an angle of 72°.

First draw a horizontal line about 6cm long
And mark a point at the right-hand end. ☞

Lay the protractor on this line.
With the center at the point and measure round from the left side To 72°.

Put a mark there and join up to the point.

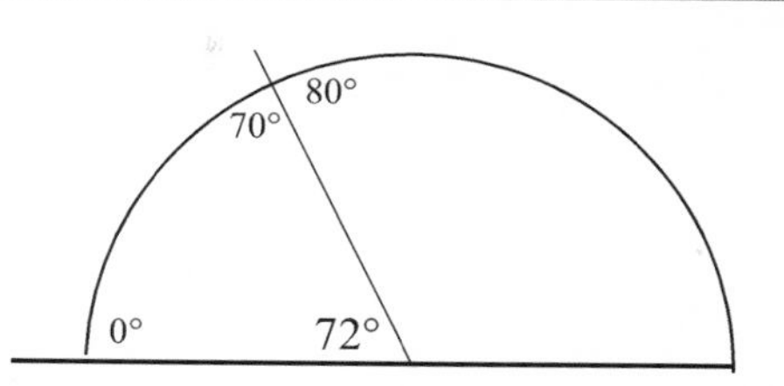

The line with which you start when you draw an angle will not always be horizontal, and the vertex will not always be at the end of the line.

EXERCISE 4

Construct angles of:

a 40° **b** 88° **c** 115° **d** 171° **e** 200° **f** 290° **g** 335°

EXERCISE 5

To plot the positions of the Sun , Moon and planets for 0^h 1st January 2000 as seen from the Earth.

a Draw a circle the same size as for Exercise 3. Mark the centre and draw in the vertical diameter.

b Put 0 at the top and, using your protractor, plot the positions given below, measuring anti-clockwise around the circle.

Jupiter 25°	Saturn 40°	Sun 280°
Moon 217°	Neptune 303°	Mercury 271°
Venus 241°	Mars 328°	Uranus 315°
Pluto 251°		

c Write the planet names on your diagram.

ANGLES IN A TRIANGLE

❋ Draw a triangle in your book: do not make it too small.
❋ Measure all 3 angles of your triangle and add up the 3 numbers.
❋ Compare your answer to the answer your friends have got.
You should find that everyone has an answer of 180° or close to that.
❋ Try to make a triangle whose angles do not add up to 180°.

❋ Take a sheet of paper and carefully cut out a triangle.
With one side as base, fold the top angle over so that it just touches the base but position it along the base line so that the fold you make is parallel to the base line. Then fold the other two angles over so that they all meet at the same point.

You should find that whatever shape of triangle you started with the three angles now form a straight line. And since the angle in a straight line is 180° this demonstrates (By completing the rectangle and *By Mere Observation*) that:

the angles of any triangle add up to 180°.

We will see a proper proof of this important theorem later.

One consequence of this result is that if we know two angles of a triangle we can calculate the third angle.

EXAMPLE 3

Find the angles marked with a letter:

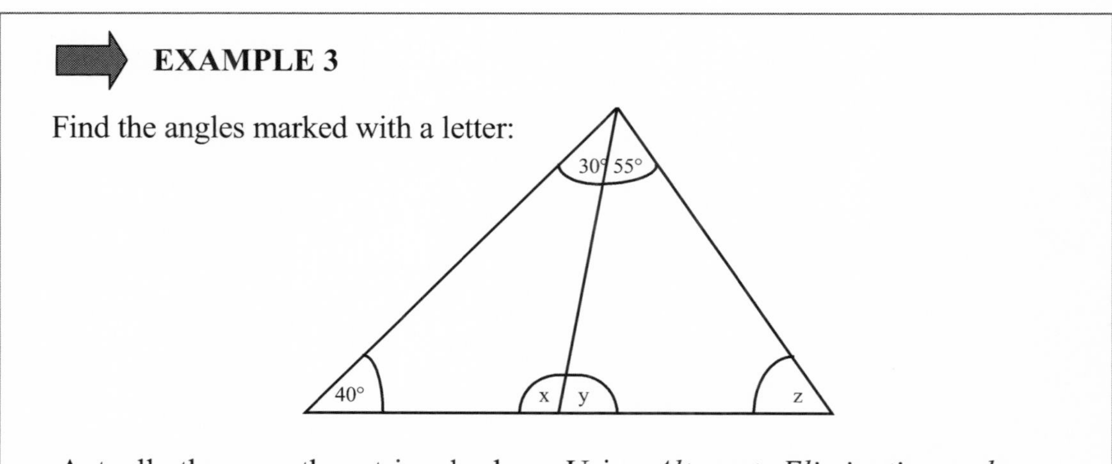

Actually there are three triangles here. Using *Alternate Elimination and Retention* we look first at the triangle on the left. ☞

Since we know two angles we can find the third since they total 180°.
So *By Addition and by Subtraction* gives 70° for the two given angles and then 110° for the third. So x = 110°.

Now x and y complete a half circle, which is 180°.
So y must be 180 – 110 = 70. y = 70°.

Finally we can get z either from the triangle on the right or from the whole triangle which contains the two smaller ones.
So 55 + 70 = 125 and 180 – 125 = 55. So z = 55°.

❋ Check that the angles making up the big triangle add up to 180°.

EXERCISE 6

Find the angles marked with letters:

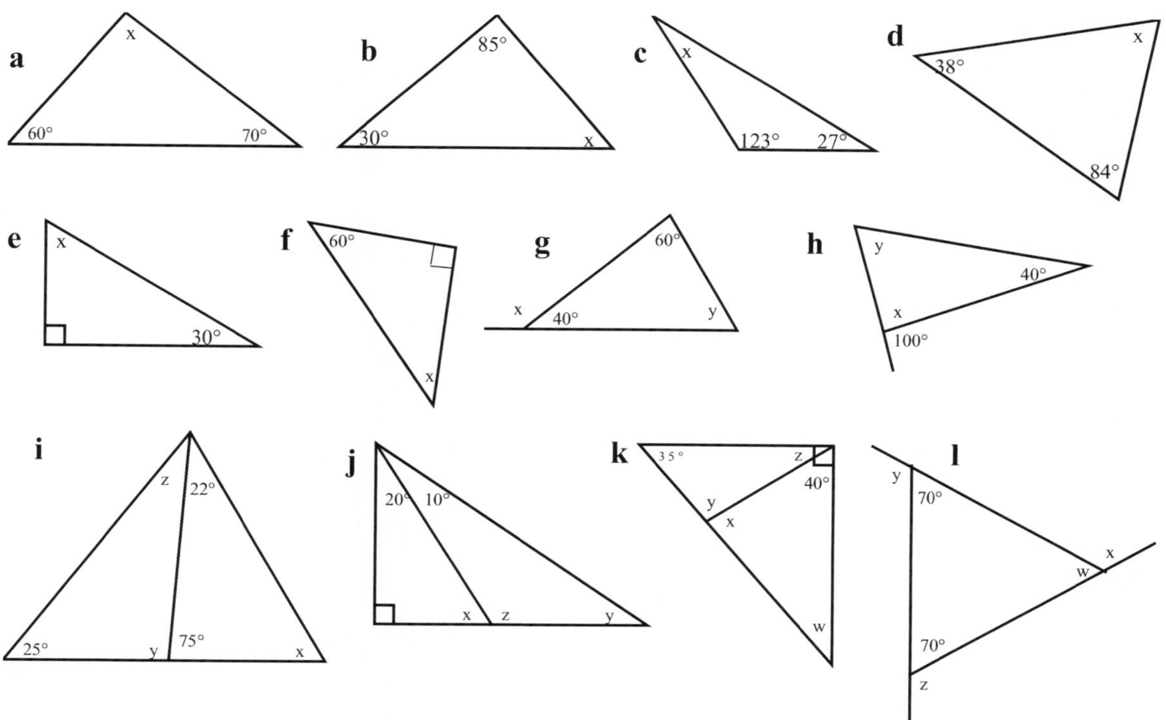

CONSTRUCTING TRIANGLES

A triangle has 3 sides and 3 angles.
We do not need to know all these in order to draw the triangle.
What is the minimum amount of information needed to be able to construct a triangle?

If we were given the lengths of 3 sides of a triangle there is only one triangle that can be made with those lengths, so we can construct the triangle.

Given 3 angles of a triangle, however, we could not construct it as we do not know any sizes: we know the shape, but not the size.

Given the base c, and the two base angles, a and b, defines a triangle, as we could construct it by drawing the base, then the base angles, which can then be extended until they meet at the apex.

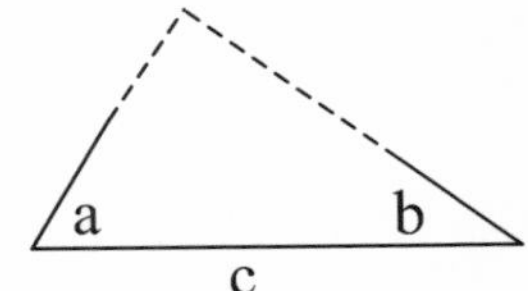

Being given two sides, L and M, and the angle A, between tem also defines a particular triangle, because we could draw one of the sides as a base, construct the given angle at one end and extend the second arm of the angle until its length equals that of the other given side.

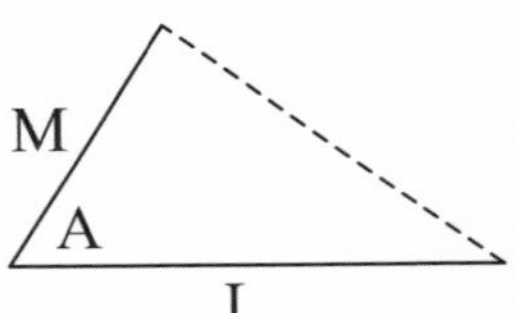

There are other possibilities too as the following example shows.

EXAMPLE 4

Construct a triangle with a base of 3cm, a base angle of 73° and the side opposite this base angle of 4cm.

A sketch shows that the triangle can be drawn:

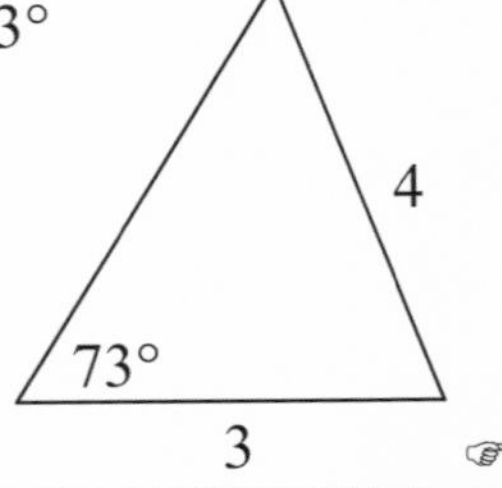

☞

We begin by drawing the base line 3cm long.
Then draw the angle at 73°.
Next we want a point on this line 4cm from C.
For accuracy we set our compasses at 4cm, put the point on C and draw an arc which cuts the line AB.
This gives the position of A which we then join to C.

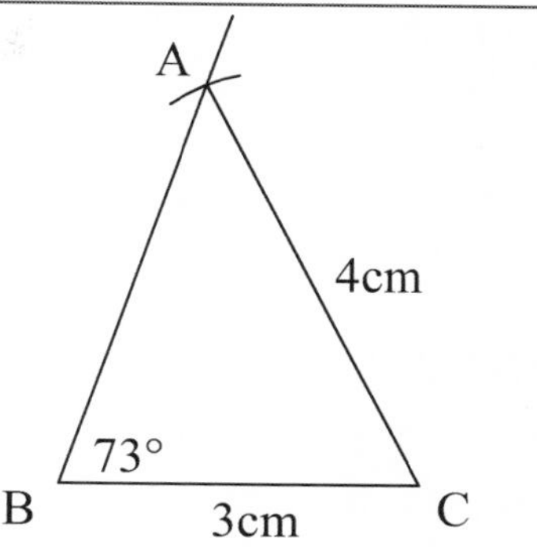

EXERCISE 7

Use ruler and protractor to draw the following triangles and in **f g h i** use compasses as well (it is worth drawing a sketch first if the method is not clear):

a Base 6cm, base angles 37° and 43°.

b Base 9cm, base angles 22° and 97°.

c Base 14cm, base angles 47° and 73°.

d Sides 6cm and 4cm and the angle between them 37°.

e Sides 6cm and 3cm and the angle between them 72°.

f Sides 6cm, 4cm and 3cm.

g Sides 5cm, 4cm and 3cm.

h Base 2.5cm, base angle 125° and side opposite this base angle of 5cm.

i Base 4cm, base angle 30° and side opposite this base angle of 3cm. (2 answers)

j Base 4cm, a base angle of 40° and an apex angle of 50°.
(Remember, the angles of a triangle add up to 180°)

k Base 6cm, a base angle of 37° and an apex angle of 41°.

l All sides 4cm.

❋ Measure the angles in the last triangle.

You should find that all the angles are 60° or close to this. This is because the triangle is an equilateral triangle: it has all sides and all angles equal.

1 What would you expect the angles of a triangle with all sides 7cm to be?

ISOSCELES TRIANGLES

An isosceles triangle is one with two sides equal: we have met these before.

EXAMPLE 5

Construct the triangle XYZ in which XY = XZ = 6cm and YZ = 5cm.
A sketch shows what is required:

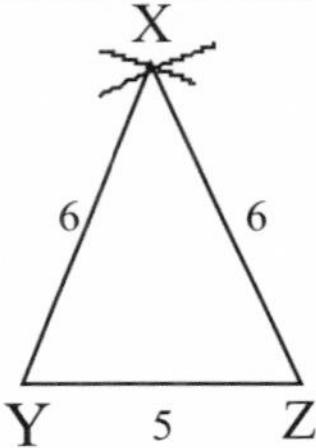

So we can begin with the base 5cm long.

Then with compasses set at 6cm we put the point on Y and Z and draw arcs where we expect the apex to be.

Where the arcs cross gives X and we can complete the triangle.

❋ Draw the triangle as described above and measure the three angles of the isosceles triangle.

You should have found that the base angles are both about 65° and that the apex angle is about 49 or 50°.

It will not be surprising that the base angles are the same because the natural symmetry of the isosceles triangle indicates this.

> An isosceles triangle has two equal sides and 2 equal angles.
> The equal angles are always at the ends of the equal sides.

Where we refer to the **apex angle** we will mean the angle where the two equal sides meet.

This is therefore the angle X in the triangle above, and the angle B in the triangle opposite.

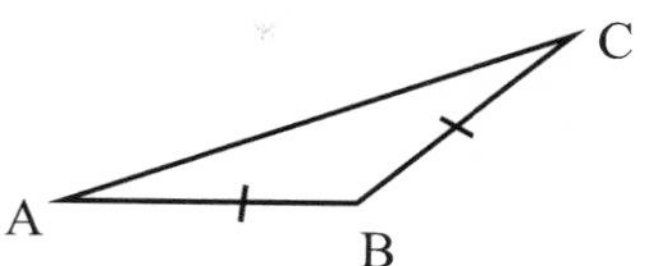

EXAMPLE 6

In the triangle ABC, AB = AC, BC = 3cm and $\hat{A}$ = 100°.
Construct the triangle.
A sketch shows the required figure:

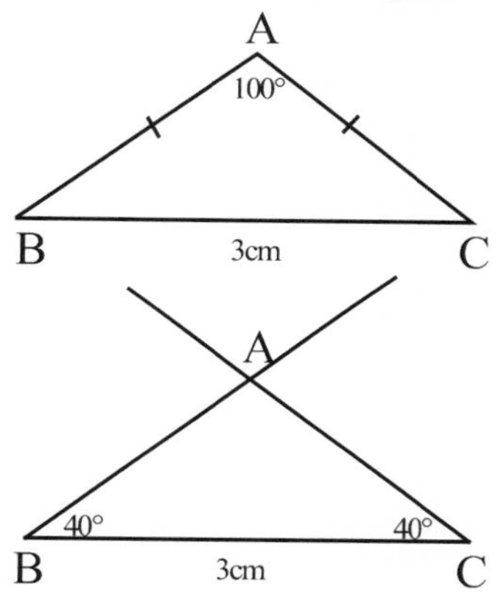

But since the three angles in the triangle add up to 180° if the top angle is 100° the angles at B, C must add up to 80°. And since the angles are equal they must be 40° each.

This means we can draw the base and construct 40° angles at each end of it.

EXERCISE 8

Construct the following triangles:

a Base 5cm, other sides 3cm, **b** base 2.3cm, other sides 4cm,

c base 4cm, base angles 30°.

Construct triangle XYZ in which:

d YZ = 3cm, XY = XZ, $\hat{X}$ = 70°, **e** XY = 6cm, ZX = ZY, angle XZY = 150°,

f the base XY = XZ = 4.5cm and $\hat{X}$ = 35°, **g** XY = XZ = 4cm and $\hat{X}$ = 140°.

2 In the diagram opposite O is the centre of the circle.
Is the triangle isosceles?
❋ Can you explain this?

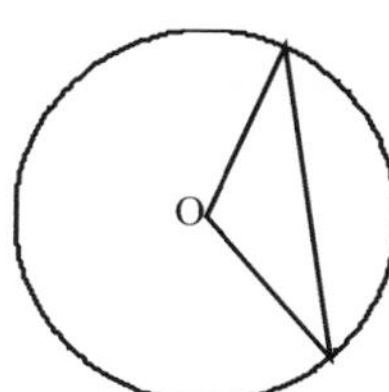

3 In the diagram opposite AB and AC are tangents to the circle.
Tangents are lines which just touch a circle without going inside.
Is the triangle isosceles?
Can you explain this?

CALCULATING ANGLES

EXAMPLE 7

Find the angles marked with letters:

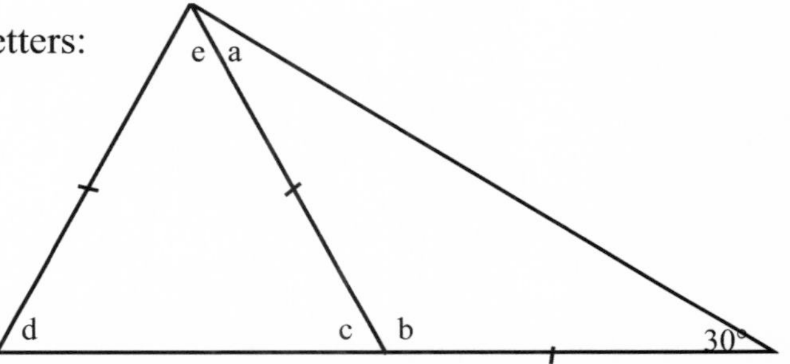

Here we see two isosceles triangles which means that there are a pair of equal angles in each triangle.

In the left-hand triangle the equal angles are d and c.
In the right-hand triangle the equal angles are (as always) at the ends of the equal sides, so a and 30° are equal: <u>a = 30°</u>.

Since the angles in a triangle add up to 180° we find that <u>b = 120°</u>.
b and c also add up to 180° so <u>c = 60°.</u>
Since d = c <u>d = 60°</u>.
And since c, d and e add up to 180° <u>e = 60°</u>.

The left-hand triangle is therefore an equilateral triangle: it has all angles (and therefore all sides) equal.

EXERCISE 9

Find the angles marked with letters:

a

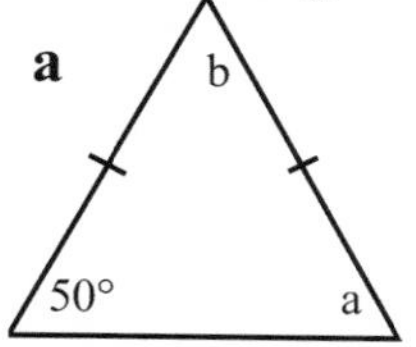

b

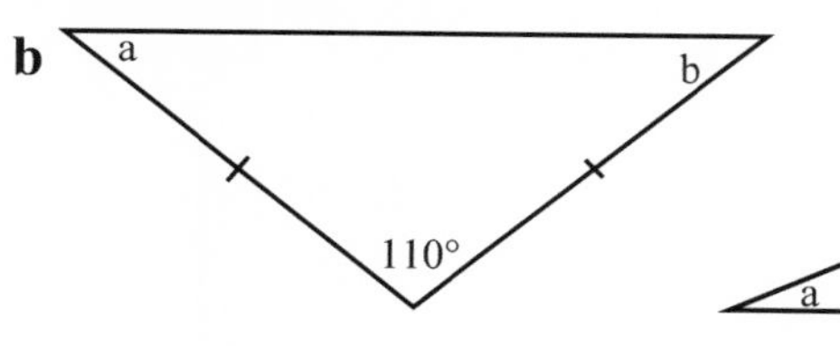

c

d

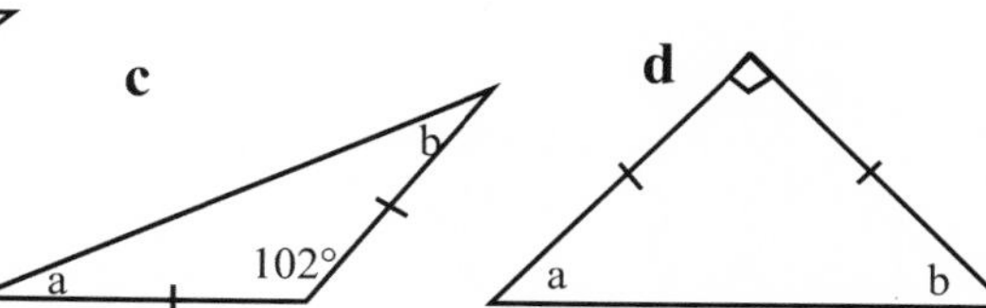

e

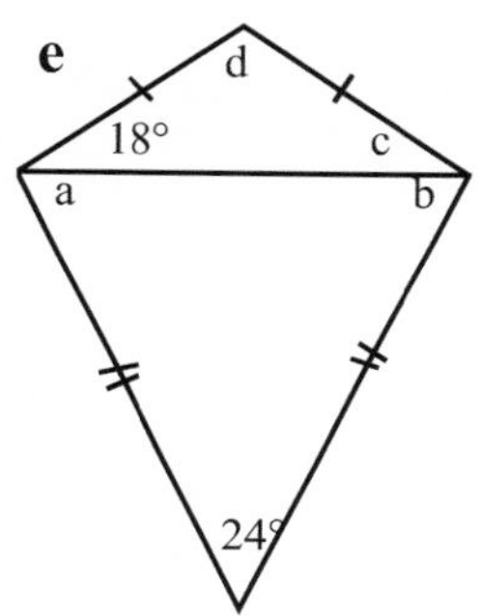

f

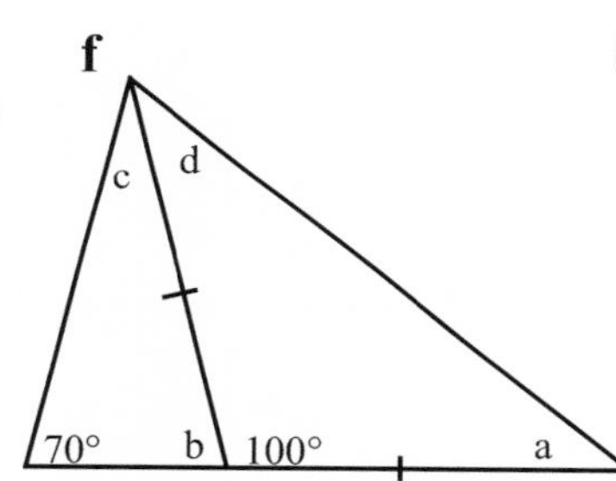

g

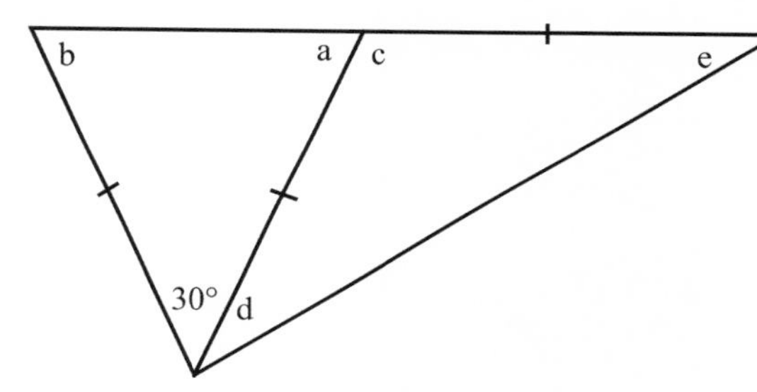

"Where there is life there is pattern and where there is pattern there is mathematics"

John D. Barrow

ASTRONOMER

14

PERCENTAGES

A percentage is simply a fraction in which the denominator is 100.

So 20% (20 per cent) means $\frac{20}{100}$. And this cancels down to $\frac{1}{5}$.
Similarly 50% means $\frac{1}{2}$, and 100% means a whole one.

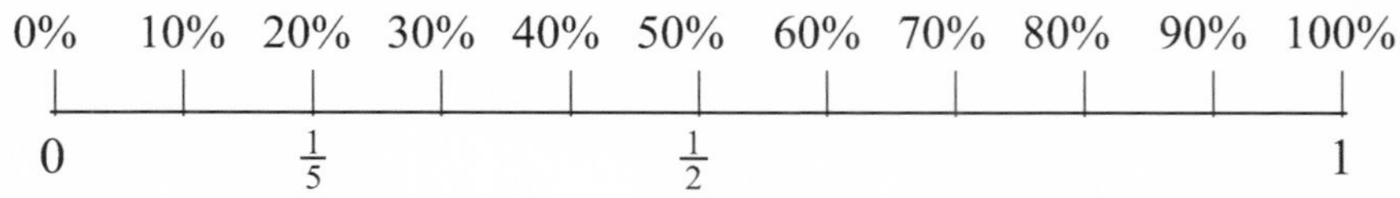

CONVERTING A PERCENTAGE TO A FRACTION

It is therefore very easy to convert percentages to fractions: we simply write the number over 100 and cancel if possible.

EXAMPLE 1

Change 15% to a fraction.

$15\% = \frac{15}{100} = \frac{3}{20}$.

We change a percentage to a fraction by dividing the number by 100.

EXAMPLE 2

Change 37½% to a fraction.

$37\frac{1}{2}\% = \frac{37\frac{1}{2}}{100} = \frac{75}{200} = \frac{3}{8}$.

Here we double the top and bottom of the fraction $\frac{37\frac{1}{2}}{100}$ to get $\frac{75}{200}$ and then cancel by 25.

EXERCISE 1

Convert the following percentages to fractions:

a 40% **b** 90% **c** 25% **d** 50% **e** 75%

f 35% **g** 5% **h** 10% **i** 56% **j** 17%

k 12½% **l** 62½% **m** $33\frac{1}{3}\%$

CONVERTING A FRACTION TO A PERCENTAGE

The reverse process is also quite easy.
We simply multiply top and bottom of the fraction (if necessary) so that we get 100 in the bottom.

EXAMPLE 3

Convert **a** $\frac{15}{100}$ **b** $\frac{8}{50}$ **c** $\frac{7}{20}$ **d** $\frac{4}{5}$ to percentages.

a $\frac{15}{100} = \underline{15\%}$

b $\frac{8}{50} = \frac{16}{100} = \underline{16\%}$

c $\frac{7}{20} = \frac{35}{100} = \underline{35\%}$

d $\frac{4}{5} = \frac{80}{100} = \underline{80\%}$

EXAMPLE 4

Convert $\frac{5}{6}$ to a percentage.

Here we cannot find a whole number to multiply 6 by to get 100.
We therefore multiply the fraction by 100 (which is just the reverse of the previous method of converting a fraction to a percentage).

$\frac{5}{6} \times 100\% = \frac{500}{6} = \frac{250}{3} = 83\frac{1}{3}\%$.

We could also have used this method in Example 3**c**: $\frac{7}{20} = \frac{7}{20} \times 100\% = \frac{700}{20}\% = 35\%$.

EXERCISE 2

Change the following to percentages:

a $\frac{85}{100}$ **b** $\frac{3}{20}$ **c** $\frac{1}{10}$ **d** $\frac{3}{4}$ **e** $\frac{24}{25}$ **f** $\frac{27}{50}$ **g** $\frac{2}{9}$ **h** $\frac{2}{3}$ **i** $\frac{1}{7}$

IMPORTANT PERCENTAGES

The following percentage equivalents are worth knowing as they arise quite frequently:

$10\% = \frac{1}{10}$ $20\% = \frac{1}{5}$ $25\% = \frac{1}{4}$ $50\% = \frac{1}{2}$ $75\% = \frac{3}{4}$ $12\frac{1}{2}\% = \frac{1}{8}$

Many percentage questions can be answered easily and mentally using these basic equivalents.

CONVERTING BETWEEN PERCENTAGES, FRACTIONS AND DECIMALS

Converting between percentages and decimals is an easy matter as the denominator of the percentage expressed as a fraction is always 100.

EXAMPLE 5

Change 65% to a decimal.

$65 \div 100 = \underline{0.65}$. (because 65% means $\frac{65}{100}$).

EXAMPLE 6

Change 0.3 to a percentage.

Here we multiply by 100: $0.3 \times 100 = 30$.
So 0.3 = 30%.

10% is a particularly useful percentage as it is $\frac{1}{10}$ as a fraction and 0.1 as a decimal.

EXERCISE 3

Copy and complete the following table (the first one has been done for you):

Percentage	Fraction	Decimal
70	$\frac{7}{10}$	0.7
15		
52		
1		
	$\frac{1}{4}$	
	$\frac{2}{5}$	
	$\frac{11}{20}$	
		0.12
		0.5
		0.13

All this comes under the Vedic formula *Proportionately*.

FINDING A PERCENTAGE OF A QUANTITY

We sometimes need to find a percentage of something, if for example we are offered a 15% discount on something we want to buy.

EXAMPLE 7

Find 20% of 70.

We can see mentally that 10% of 70 is 7, so 20% must be <u>14</u>.

EXAMPLE 8

Find 15% of 60.

Since 10% of 60 is 6, 5% will be 3. Therefore 15% must be 6 + 3 = <u>9</u>.

EXAMPLE 9

Find 7½% of 80.

Here we spot that 7½ is 3×2½. And 2½ is a quarter of 10.
10% will be 8, so 5% will be 4 and 2½% will be 12.
So 7½% of 80 will be 3×12 = <u>36</u>.

EXAMPLE 10

Find 3% of 5000.

Here we can find 1% of 5000, which is 50, then 3% must be 3×50 = <u>150</u>.

EXERCISE 4

Find:

a 10% of 90	**b** 20% of 50	**c** 30% of 300	**d** 90% of 40
e 80% of 2000	**f** 25% of 60	**g** 75% of 28	**h** 15% of 40
i 2½% of 80	**j** 70% of 500	**k** 80% of 20	**l** 20% of 80
m 45% of 60	**n** 7½% of 200	**o** 3% of 700	**p** 23% of 100
q 13% of 2000	**r** 12½% of 200	**s** 6% of 80,000	**t** 55% of 60

EXAMPLE 11

Find 7% of 3.

The best way here is to find 1% of 3 and multiply by 7.
1% of 3 is 0.03, so 7% is 7×0.03 = <u>0.21</u>.

EXAMPLE 12

Find 37% of 20.

Again we find 1% first: 1% of 20 is 0.2, so 37% is 37×0.2 = <u>7.4</u>.

EXAMPLE 13

Find 34% of 36.

1% of 36 is 0.36, so 34% is 34×0.36 and we recognise 34×36 as being easy under the formula *By One More than the One Before.*
So 34% of 36 = <u>12.24</u>.

EXERCISE 5

Find:

a 3% of 9 **b** 11% of 4 **c** 12% of 20 **d** 28% of 2 **e** 33% of 3

f 13% of 6 **g** 8% of 21 **h** 6% of 33 **i** 3% of 88 **j** 17% of 4

k 6% of 53 **l** 36% of 2 **m** 31% of 4 **n** 23% of 5

o 600 pupils sit an examination. 85% passed and 8% gained distinctions. How many passed the exam and how many obtained a distinction?

p The area of a field is 5 acres. If 20% of the field is unusable how many acres can be used?

You may have noticed in Exercise 4, **k** and **l** that the answers to 80% of 20 and 20% of 80 are the same. This is generally true, so if we had for example 37% of 20 we could use *Transpose and Apply* and find 20% of 37, knowing that it will give the same answer.

FORMING A PERCENTAGE

Sometimes we need to form our own percentages.

EXAMPLE 14

Jane got 15 marks out of 20 in a test. What percentage mark did she get?

It may be obvious from the question that Jane got three quarters of the marks. And this is equivalent to 75%.

We can also write 15 out of 20 as a fraction, $\frac{15}{20}$, and convert this to a decimal by multiplying top and bottom by 5. This gives 75%.

> To find what percentage one thing is of another we form a fraction (the first over the second) and convert this to a percentage.

EXAMPLE 15

What percentage is 20p of £3?

We must not mix the units so we will decide to work in pence:

$\frac{20}{300} \times 100\% = \frac{20}{3}\%$ (cancelling by 100),

EXERCISE 6

Find what percentage the first quantity is of the second:

a 2 of 8 **b** 9 of 12 **c** 20 of 400 **d** 6 of 15 ☞

e £1.20 of £5 **f** 20 of 1000 **g** 4cm of 1m **h** 45g of 75g

i What percentage of 20 is 8?

j What percentage of £1 is 10p?

k Alan got 56 marks out of 80 in a test. In the next test he got 45 marks out of 60. Find the percentage mark in each test. Did Alan do better in the second test or worse?

l 15cm is sawn off a board 120cm long. What percentage of the board has been removed?
What percentage is left?

❋ Find out what percentage of your class are left-handed.

❋ Find out what percentage of your class have blue eyes.

"Geometry will draw the soul towards truth..."

Plato (429–347 BC)

GREEK PHILOSOPHER

15

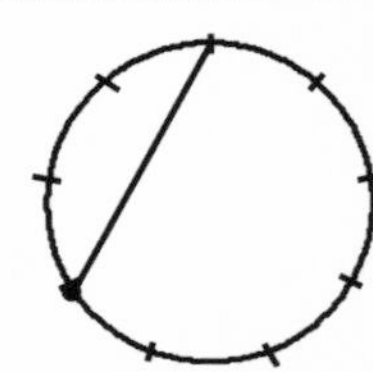

FORMING EQUATIONS

Sometimes a problem leads to an equation which we can then solve.

EXAMPLE 1

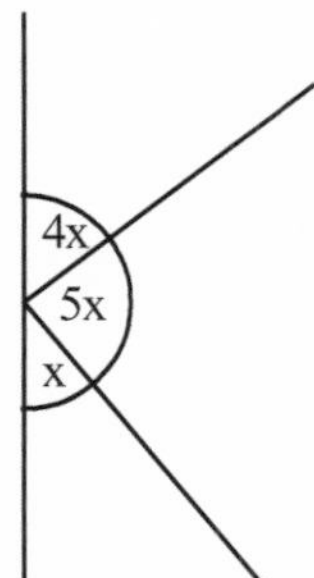

We see here that the angles form a half circle, which is 180°.

We can therefore say: $4x + 5x + x = 180$

So $10x = 180$
and $x = 18$.

And if $x = 18$, $4x = 72$ and $5x = 90$. So the angles must be 72°, 90° 18°. We may check that these angles do actually add up to 180°.

EXAMPLE 2

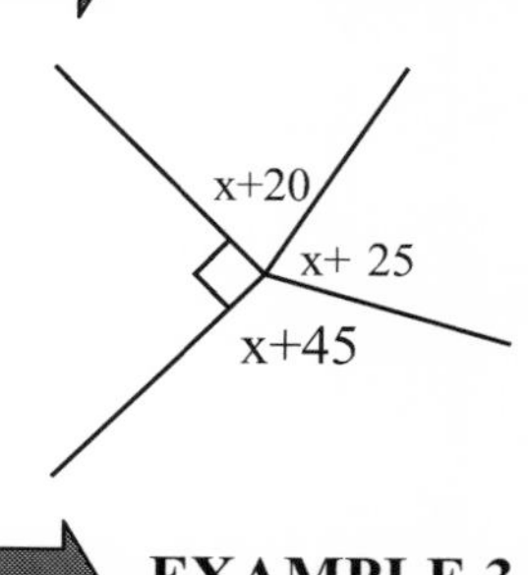

Here the four angles total 360°, and one of them is a right angle.

So $90 + x+20 + x+25 + x+45 = 360$
Then we add the x terms and the numbers up:
$3x + 180 = 360$.
So $\underline{x = 60.}$
<u>The angles are therefore 90°, 80°, 85° and 105°.</u>

EXAMPLE 3

Find the angles:

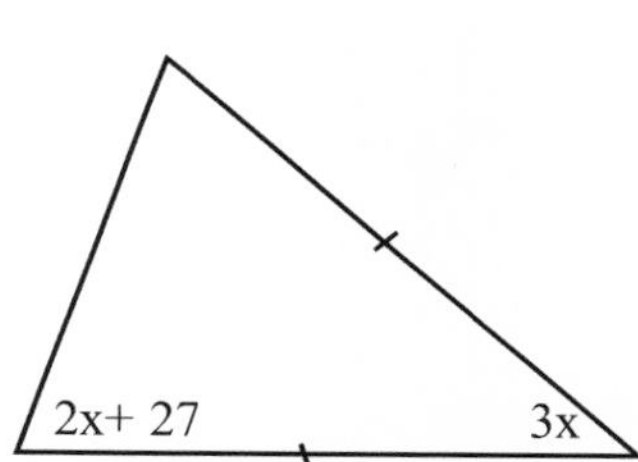

Since the triangle is isosceles the third angle must be $2x+27$ also.

So $2x+27 + 2x+27 + 3x = 180$

And $7x + 54 = 180$

So $x = 18$ and the angles are 54°, 63°, 63°.

EXERCISE 1

Find x and the size of the angles:

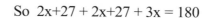

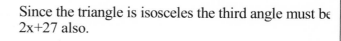

a

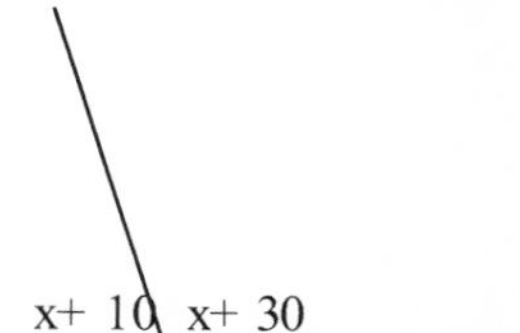

b

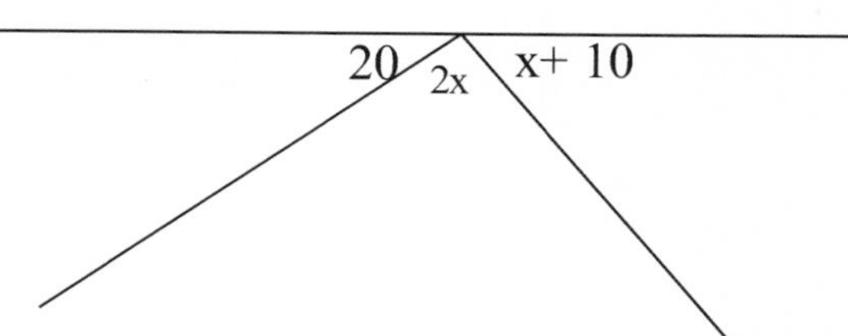

c

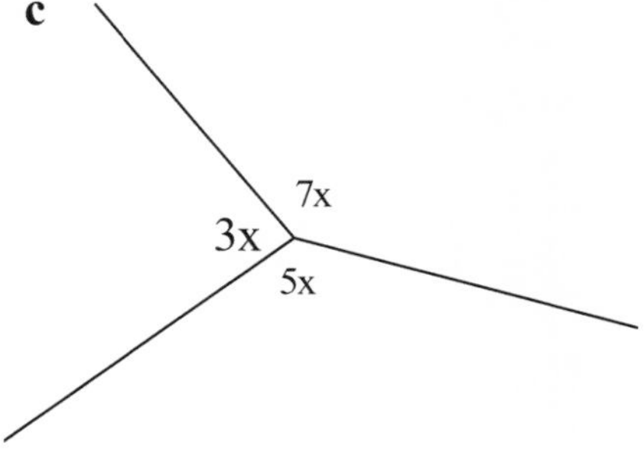

d

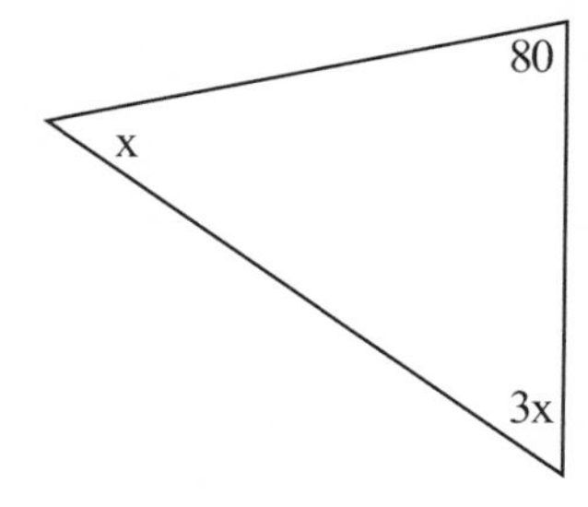

☞

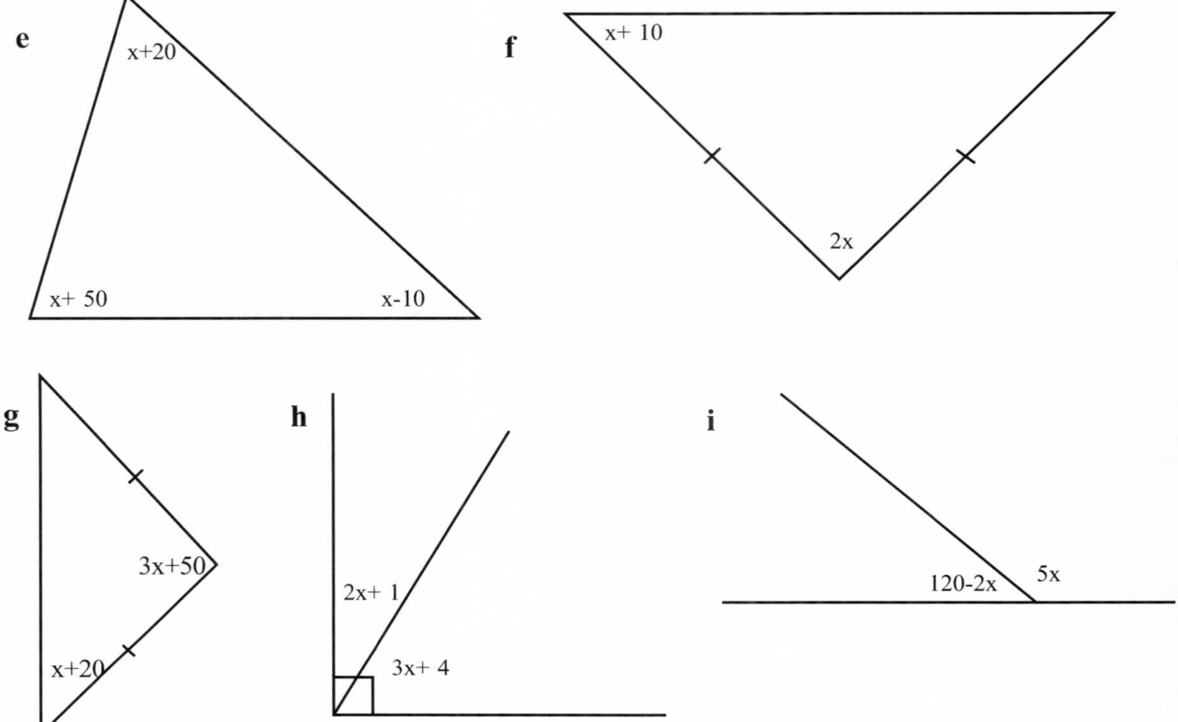

EXAMPLE 4

A rectangle has a base of 3x+5 and a height of 4 units.
Find x given that **a** its perimeter is 48, **b** its area is 104.

a If the perimeter is 48: $3x+5 + 3x+5 + 4 + 4 = 48$

$6x + 18 = 48,$

$\underline{x = 5}.$

4

3x+5

b Since the area of a rectangle is base×height, $(3x+5)\times 4 = 104.$

Dividing both sides by 4: $3x + 5 = 26,$

$\underline{x = 7}.$

EXERCISE 2

Find x in each of the following:

a An isosceles triangle has two sides of length x and one of length x+3 and its perimeter is 21.

b A triangle has sides x, x+2 and x+4 and its perimeter is 24.

c A right-angled triangle has a base of 2x–1, a height of 8 and its area is 60.

d A triangle has a base of 10, height x and its area is 30.

e An isosceles triangle has sides x, x, x+3 and its perimeter is 63.

f A rectangle has a base of 3, a height of 2x+1 and its area is 63.

g A number, x, when doubled and increased by 5 gives 39. Write down an equation for x and solve it.

h A number, x, is trebled and then reduced by 17. If this gives a result of 73 write down an equation for x and solve it.

i A number, x, is reduced by 3 and then doubled to give 24. Write down an equation for x and solve it.

"Behold the heaven, the earth, the sea; all that is bright in them or above them; all that creep or fly or swim; all have forms because all have number. Take away number and they will be nothing... Ask what delights you in dancing and number will reply: 'Lo, here I am.' Examine the beauty of bodily form, and you will find that everything is in its place by number. Examine the beauty of bodily motion and you will find everything in its due time by number.

St Augustine (354 – 430 AD)

16

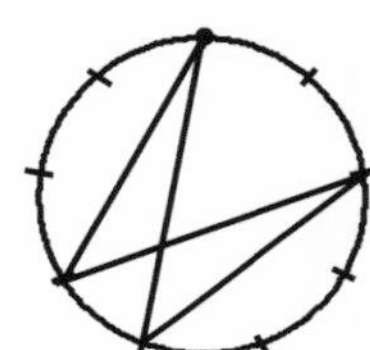

2 AND 3-DIMENSIONAL SHAPES

DIMENSIONS

A straight line is said to be 1-dimensional because it has only one direction, or two directions if you think of it having two opposite directions.
A pencil is rather like a 1-dimensional object because it is like a straight line.

❋ Name some other objects which look 1-dimensional.

A flat area, like a table top or wall, is called a **plane**.
It is said to be 2-dimensional because 2 perpendicular straight lines can be placed in it. Triangles and rectangles are 2-dimensional shapes.

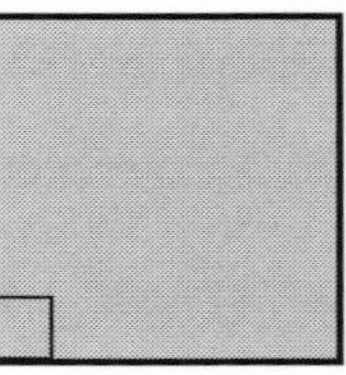

❋ Name some other objects which look 2-dimensional.

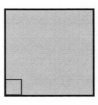

Solid or hollow objects like a **cube** or **sphere** (ball shape) are examples of 3-dimensional forms. They can contain 3 perpendicular straight lines, like OA, OB, OC opposite.

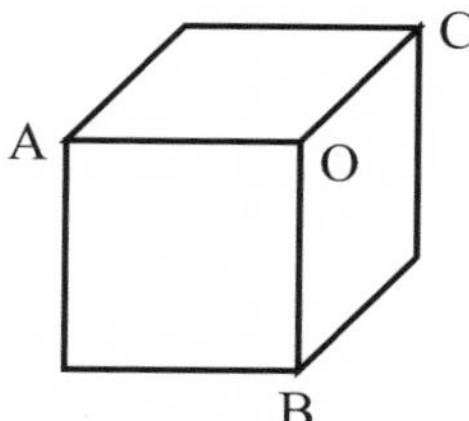

Name some other objects which look 3-dimensional.

Sometimes it is not obvious what dimension applies to a form:
There are forms which are both 1 and 2-dimensional, like a wavy line drawn on paper,

or 1 and 3-dimensional, like a helix (shaped like a spiral staircase),
or 2 and 3-dimensional, like the surface of a sphere.

2-DIMENSIONAL SHAPES

First let us revise our work on 2-dimensional shapes and area.
You will need a sheet of A4 graph paper.

1 Using the bold lines on the graph paper draw a rectangle 18cm by 28cm. Along the bottom edge, which should be the 28cm edge, number the centimetre marks from 0 (in the corner) to 28 (you may number every two cm if you wish). Number from 0 to 18 up the left-hand side (in 2's if you wish).

You will remember that a point can be described by two coordinates, like (4,18). Put a small cross at the point (4,18). That is, starting at the bottom left-hand corner (the origin) go 4 units to the right and then 18 units up.

Next you are going to plot a series of points, but as each one is drawn join it to the last point plotted. (4,18) is the first point (do not attempt to plot all the points first, and then join them up).

EXERCISE 1

Join to the previous point:

a (4,8) **b** (0,8) **c** (4,0) **d** (4,4) **e** (2,4) **f** (9,18) **g** (18,18)

☞

h (9,0) **i** (4,4) **j** (24,4) **k** (24,18) **l** (14,10) **m** (24,4) **n** (28,0)

o (15,0) **p** (15,4) **q** (11,4) **r** (11,0)

You should now find that your sheet in divided into various shapes: triangles and quadrilaterals.

There is a square,
a rectangle,
2 trapezia,
a parallelogram,
5 right-angled triangles,
an isosceles triangle, and
4 other triangles.

Write the correct name inside each shape.

You may recall that:
the area of a square, rectangle or parallelogram is **base × perpendicular height**,
and that the area of a triangle is ½ **base × perpendicular height**.

EXERCISE 2

Find the area of:

a the square **b** the rectangle **c** the right-angled triangles

d the trapezia **e** the isosceles triangle **f** the other triangles

and write the answer inside the shape. You will need to split the trapezia up into a rectangle and a triangle, and for the last 5 triangles you may need to turn your sheet around.

g Now find the area of the large rectangle that contains all the shapes and use this number to find the area of the parallelogram using *By Addition and By Subtraction.*

h Check that your answer is about right by measuring the base and perpendicular height to the nearest centimetre and multiplying them.

3-DIMENSIONAL SHAPES

❋ On another A4 graph sheet, and with the long side at the bottom, draw a horizontal line across the **middle** of the page so that there are 9cm above it and 9cm below it.

Next draw a vertical line through the middle of the page so that there are 14cm on each side.

Put O at the intersection of the lines. This point is the Origin.

As before each centimetre is counted as 1 so number to the right of O from 1 to 14.
Just like the **number line** we have seen before we can now number to the left of O from $\bar{1}$ to $\overline{14}$
Now number upwards from O from 1 to 9, and then downwards from O from $\bar{1}$ to $\bar{9}$.

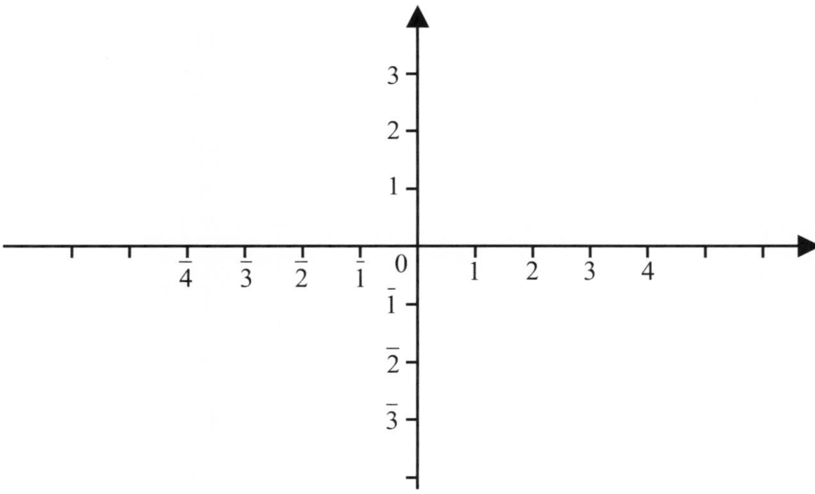

You should have an extended version of the diagram shown above. This allows us to extend our graphs to include bar numbers.

As we have seen to plot the point D(1,7) for example we go 1 unit to the right of O and 7 units up and put a cross there with a D beside it.

EXERCISE 3

a Plot the point D as described and also the points E(2,8) and F(2,9).
Join them up to make a triangle.

Now we plot the point A($\bar{2}$,7), which means 2 units to the left of O and 7 units up.
Plot also the points B($\bar{1}$,8) and C($\bar{1}$,9) and join them to form another triangle.

Now join A to D, C to F and B to E.
This should look like a 3-dimensional shape: it is called a **triangular prism**.
Write this to the left of the figure.

b Next we will plot a **hexagonal prism**.
Plot the point A(8,5) and, joining each point to the previous point plot B(9,5), C(10,6), D(9,8), E(8,8), F(7,7) and join F to A.

Plot G(11,9), H(12,9), I(13,7), J(12,6) joining G to H, H to I and I to J.

Now join BJ, CI, DH and EG.
Write the name on the left.

A prism is a 3-dimensional object which is the same shape all the way through: the first shape was a triangle all the way through, and the second shape is a hexagon all the way through.

c For the point A with coordinates ($\bar{8}$,$\bar{9}$) we go 8 units to the left of O and 9 units down.

Plot A and the points B($\bar{6}$,$\bar{9}$), C($\bar{6}$,$\bar{7}$), D($\bar{8}$,$\bar{7}$). Join these to make a square.
Plot E($\bar{7}$,$\bar{6}$), F($\bar{5}$,$\bar{6}$), G($\bar{5}$,$\bar{8}$) and join EF and FG.
Join DE, CF and BG to complete the shape.
Write **cube** on the left.

The point A together with the points H($\bar{4}$,$\bar{9}$), I($\bar{4}$,$\bar{5}$, J($\bar{8}$,$\bar{5}$), L($\bar{6}$,$\bar{3}$), M($\bar{2}$,$\bar{7}$) form another cube identical to the first but twice the size. Draw the larger cube in.

☞

d The points for the next shape use all four sections of the graph. Remember, the first coordinate is found on the horizontal axis (horizontal number line) and the second coordinate tells you how far to go up or down.
Plot A($\overline{2}$,$\overline{2}$), B(1,$\overline{2}$), C(1,1), D($\overline{2}$,1). Join these to form a square.

Plot E(4,5), F(7,5), G(7,2) and join EF and FG.
Join DE, CF and BG.
Write the name **cuboid** below the shape.
A cuboid is like a cube but the sides are not all the same length.

We can also draw in the hidden edges if we like: plot H(4,2) and join HA, HE, HG with a **dashed** line. Hidden lines are usually drawn dashed.

e Plot O(9,3), A(8,1), B(9½,1), C(10,2).
Join O to A, B and C.
Join AB, BC.

This is a **triangular pyramid** or **tetrahedron.**

There is a hidden line, AC. Draw a dashed line from A to C.

O is a **vertex** (corner) of the pyramid. A, B and C are also **vertices.**

Another pyramid twice the size of OABC is to be drawn with the same vertex, O.
The other vertices are at (7, $\overline{1}$), (10, $\overline{1}$) and (11,1).
Draw in the second pyramid, including the hidden line.

A third pyramid three times the size of the first also has vertex O and vertices at (6, $\overline{3}$), (10½,$\overline{3}$) and (12,0). Draw it in.

Draw in a fourth pyramid, which is four times the size of the first, and write down the coordinates of the 3 vertices of the base (write on your graph paper).

Write "tetrahedron or triangular pyramid" below your final diagram.

f The vertices of a **rectangular-based pyramid** are O($\overline{9\frac{1}{2}}$,6), A($\overline{10}$,4), B($\overline{9}$,4), C($\overline{8}$,5).
Plot these points.

☞

Note that $\overline{9\tfrac{1}{2}}$ is $\tfrac{1}{2}$ to the **right** of $\overline{10}$.

Join O to A, B and C, and join AB and BC.

There is a hidden vertex at D($\overline{9}$,5). Plot this point and draw in the hidden lines DA, DC and OD.

A pyramid twice the size of the first has vertices at O and ($\overline{10\tfrac{1}{2}}$,2), ($\overline{8\tfrac{1}{2}}$,2), ($\overline{6\tfrac{1}{2}}$,4), ($\overline{8\tfrac{1}{2}}$,4).
Draw this pyramid with the hidden lines also shown.

Draw in a third pyramid three times the size of the first and with vertex O (extend the lines you have already and use the squares on the graph paper to help you).
Write down the coordinates of the 4 corners of the base.

Finally repeat for a fourth pyramid, four times the size of the first.
Write "square-base pyramid" below.

Two other important 3-dimensional forms are the **cylinder** and the **cone**.

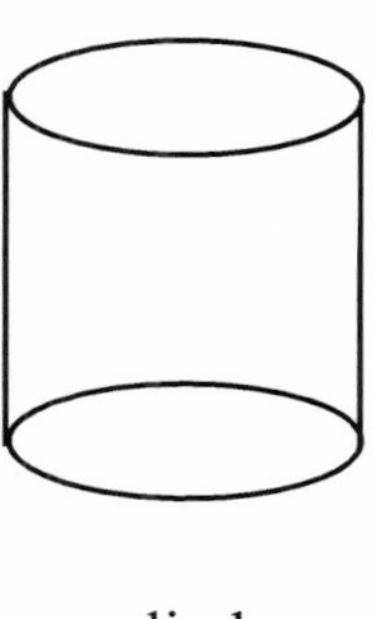

cylinder

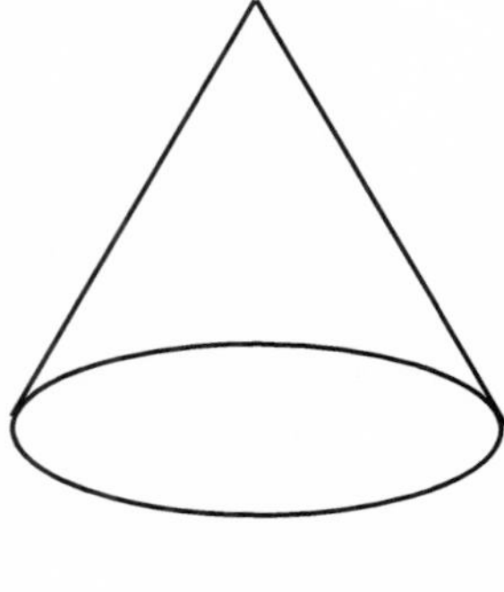

cone

"I was especially delighted with the mathematics, on account of the certitude and evidence of their reasonings; but I had not as yet a precise knowledge of their true use..."

René Descartes (1596–1650)

FRENCH PHILOSOPHER AND MATHEMATICIAN

17

STRAIGHT LINE GRAPHS

The idea of converting an algebraic equation into a geometrical form came in recent times from the French philosopher and mathematician René Descartes in 1637.
Thus Descartes showed a remarkable way of combining Arithmetic, Algebra and Geometry.

❋ On a sheet of graph paper draw a horizontal line and a vertical line, just as you did when you drew the 3-dimensional shapes, and number from $\overline{12}$ to 12 on the horizontal line and from $\overline{8}$ to 8 on the vertical line.

The horizontal line is called the **x-axis**,
and the vertical line is called the **y-axis.**

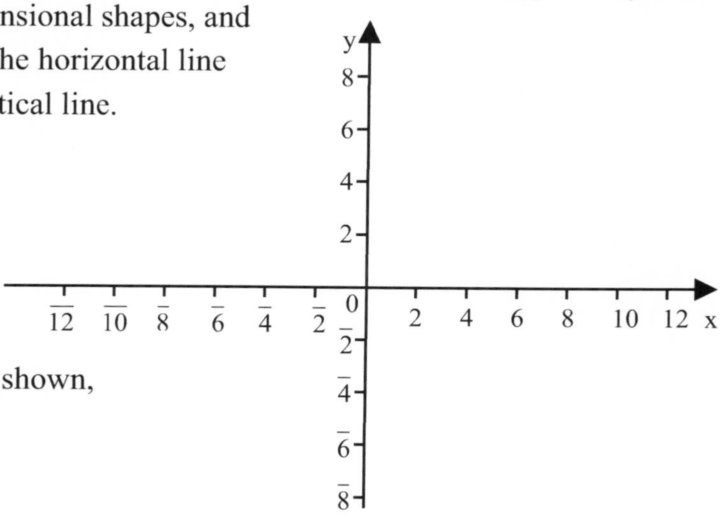

Put these on your diagram, as shown, including the arrowheads.

EXERCISE 1

a Suppose first of all that we want to draw the equation x=10.

For this you must find where x=10 on the x-axis and then draw a vertical line through this point.
Do this and write "x=10" above it.

This is the line corresponding to x=10 since for any point on the line the first coordinate (the x coordinate) is always 10.

Mark a point on the line and write down its coordinates beside it. You should find that the x coordinate (that is the first number) is 10 whichever point you choose.

b Draw the line $x = \bar{8}$.

Find $\bar{8}$ on the x-axis and draw a vertical line right across the page.
Write the equation above the line.

Check that it is right by writing down the coordinates of a point on the line: whatever point you choose you should find that the first coordinate is $\bar{8}$.

c Draw y = 6.

To plot this equation find the point on the y-axis where y=6 and draw a **horizontal line** right across the page through this point. Write "y=6" on it.

Choose a point on the line and write its coordinates beside it.
The y-coordinate of this point should be 6 whatever point you chose.

d Draw and label the line $y = \bar{5}$.

Find $\bar{5}$ on the y-axis and draw a horizontal line through it.
Choose a point on the line and write its coordinates beside it. Check the y-coordinate is $\bar{5}$.

> So all lines with equation **x = a** are vertical lines, and all lines with equation **y = b** are horizontal.

The equation of the y-axis will therefore be x = 0.

1 What do you think the equation of the x-axis will be?

SLOPING LINES

Next we consider equations which involve both x and y.

EXERCISE 2

a We will now draw the line $\underline{y = x}$.

Whatever value x has, y will have the same value, since $y=x$.
If $x = 1$ then $y = 1$. If $x = 3$, $y = 3$ and so on.
$x = 1$, $y = 1$ can be plotted on the graph: it is the point (1,1).
Similarly $x = 3$, $y = 3$ is plotted at (3,3).

Also $y = x$ gives the points (8,8), (0,0), $(\bar{6},\bar{6})$.

Plot these 5 points on your graph paper, they should lie in a straight but sloping line.
Draw a line through them and write the equation of the line at one end.

b We will now draw the line $\underline{y = x + 3}$.

As before we can choose any value for x (but it should be one which is on the x-axis of your graph.

If $x = 1$ then since $y = x+3$
$y = 1+3 = 4$ so we get the point (1,4). Plot this point.

If $x=2$ $y = x+3$ gives
$y = 2+3=5$ which gives the point (2,5). Plot this point.

We can show these results more neatly by making a table:

y = x + 3

x	–5	–4	–3	–2	–1	0	1	2	3	4	5
y							4	5			

The top row shows the values of x we choose.
The bottom row shows the corresponding y values.

The values we found above for x=1 and x=2 have been put in.

Copy the table into your book and fill in the remaining boxes.
Remember since y = x+3 the y value is always just 3 more than the x value, so you are just adding 3 to all the numbers in the top row.

Next we can plot each number pair as a point on the graph.
So the first point will be $(\bar{5},\bar{2})$, from the first column of your table, and so on.
This will give you 11 points on your graph, which should make a straight line.

Draw in the line and put the equation by it.

> This method of making a table, choosing some x values and finding the y value that goes with each x value, can be used for drawing all equations involving x and y.

It is worth noticing the patterns in the table above: for example, the values are increasing consecutively in both rows.

We do not actually need 11 points to draw the line in. What is the fewest number of points needed to be able to draw a line?

If we know that the line is straight then two points are enough to draw the line.

c Draw the line <u>y = x – 2</u>.

First choose a value for x, say x = 8.
Then since y = x–2, y = 8–2 = 6.
This gives the point (8,6) which we plot. The line goes through this point.

Next choose another x value, say $x = \bar{5}$.
Then $y = \bar{5} - 2 = \bar{7}$.
So we plot the point $(\bar{5},\bar{7})$ and draw a line through the two points, extended right across the page.

Find three more points of your own for this equation: choose x, find y and plot the point. Do this three times.
The points you plot should also lie on the line, confirming that the other points were correct and that y = x–2 is the equation of a **straight** line.

d Draw the line <u>y = –x</u>.

If x = 7 then y = –7 so we can plot (7, $\bar{7}$).
If x = $\bar{5}$ then y = –$\bar{5}$ = 5 so we plot ($\bar{5}$,5).
If x = 0 then y = 0 so we plot (0,0),

Check with three more points of your own, and draw in and label the line.

So the method for drawing these lines is to choose values for x, find y and plot the point. Then repeat this for other values of x.

It is best to find at least three points so that if one is wrong a correction can be made because any two points will give a line and if one point is wrong you would not know.

Do not choose the values of x too close together: the line is more accurate if the points are farther apart.

And if the y value found is not on the page you will have to choose a different x value.

Draw the following lines on the same graph page as before (do the calculations mentally):

e y = –x + 5 **f** y = 8 – x **g** y = –x – 3

❋ Study all the sloping lines you have drawn to see what connections there are between the equations and the lines.

Check that you agree with the following:

A) Equations with a "–x" term slope downwards to the right, **B)** The other equations slope upwards to the right. **C)** In each equation the term which does not contain x gives the y value where the line crosses the y-axis.

So, for example, in the equation $y = x - 2$ we have a "+x" and a "–2".
The "+x" tells us that the line slopes upwards to the right,
and the "–2" tells us that the line goes through –2 on the y-axis.

We say the **intercept** on the y-axis is –2.
❋ Check with your graph that you agree with this.

> Another word for slope is **gradient.**
> We say that lines sloping **upwards** to the right have a **positive gradient**, and lines sloping **downwards** to the right have a **negative gradient**.

❋ Draw up some new axes now on a new page. Use the same numbering as before.

EXERCISE 3

a We will now plot the graph of <u>$y = -2x$</u>

As before we choose three x values.
If $x = 4$ then $y = \bar{8}$,
if $x = 0$ then $y = 0$,
if $x = \bar{4}$ then $y = 8$.
So plot the points $(4,\bar{8})$, $(0,0)$, $(\bar{4},8)$.
You should get a straight line, which you can draw in.
Plot the following lines. Do the calculations in your head:

b $y = 2x$ **c** $y = 3x$ **d** $y = -3x$ **e** $y = x$

f $y = -x$ **g** $y = \frac{1}{2}x$ **h** $y = -\frac{1}{2}x$

You should find that you have 8 lines on your page, all going through the origin at (0,0).

On the previous graph all the sloping lines had the same steepness, the same gradient.
But here we find that the lines have different gradients.

So we see that **the effect of varying the coefficient of x is to vary the gradient**.

GRADIENT SQUARES

❋ Look carefully at the diagram below which contains lines with different slopes.

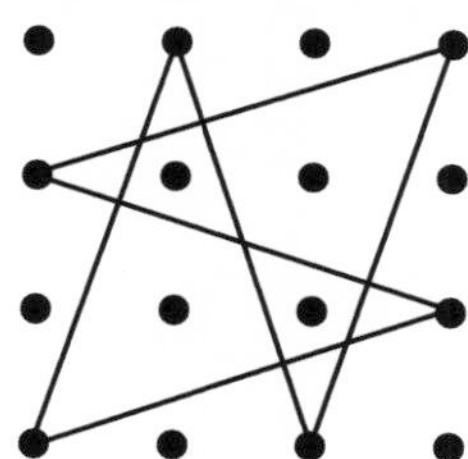

Notice that each line is a diagonal which goes 3 units horizontally and 1 unit vertically or else 3 units vertically and 1 horizontally.

EXERCISE 4

a On square spotty paper copy this diagram starting at the top right-hand corner and joining each line to the previous line.

b On the same square draw a similar pattern with the same slopes but starting at the top left corner.

c Your next gradient square will be on a 3 by 3 square of 9 dots. But this time the diagonals will be **2** units by **1** unit. Starting at the top right you should be able to draw eight continuous lines with these diagonals, ending up at the point at which you started.

d The next gradient square is on a 5 by 5 square of dots. Start again at the top right and use diagonals which are **4** units by **1** unit. You should end up where you started after 16 lines.

e On a 4 by 4 square of dots and starting at the top right draw as many joined lines as you can which are **2** units by **1** unit (you are doing well if you get 18 or more).

GRADIENTS: BY THE COMPLETION OF THE TRIANGLE

❋ Mark the point (4,4) on your graph. This point is on the line y = x.
Draw a horizontal line to the right from here. Make it 1cm long.
Then from the right end of that line draw a vertical line upwards until it meets the line y = x.

You now have a small triangle with a base of 1.

❋ What is the height of this triangle?

The height should be 1cm, and so we say that the gradient of the line y=x is 1.

❋ Do you think we would get the same answer if we had started at a different point on the line, say (8,8) or $(\bar{6},\bar{6})$?

In fact the gradient will be the same wherever you draw your triangle.

❋ Now do the same thing with the line y = 2x. Mark the point (2,4),
draw a line 1cm to the right,
draw a line upwards to complete the triangle.

Since the height of this triangle is 2, the gradient of the line y=2x is 2.

❋ Now take the line $y = -\frac{1}{2}x$. Mark a point on it, say $(4, \bar{2})$,
draw a line 1cm to the right,
draw a line downwards to complete the triangle.

The height of this triangle is $-\frac{1}{2}$ because we have to go **downwards** $\frac{1}{2}$ cm to complete the triangle.
So the gradient of $y = -\frac{1}{2}x$ is $-\frac{1}{2}$.

You may have noticed by now that **the gradient of the line is just the coefficient of x** in each equation.
Check with the other lines on your page that this is true, by drawing a suitable triangle for each line.

GRADIENT AND INTERCEPT

Now consider the equation $\underline{y = 2x - 10}$.

In this equation we know that the gradient is 2 and that the intercept on the y-axis is –10.
This information is all we need to draw the line.

EXERCISE 5

Take a new graph page but this time have the shorter edge at the bottom. The axes will go in the same place as before, but now the x-axis will be numbered from $\overline{8}$ to 8, and the y-axis from $\overline{12}$ up to 12.

a Mark the point $\overline{10}$ on the y-axis: this is the intercept of $y=2x-10$ on the y-axis.

Now we know the line has a gradient of 2 so draw a line 1cm to the right and 2cm up and complete the triangle. The sloping line shows the direction of the line you are looking for. Extend this line across the page. Try to ensure that for each 1cm the line goes to the right it goes 2cm up.

Your line should go through 5 on the x-axis.

b For the equation $\underline{y = -3x + 8}$ we start at 8 on the y-axis, go 1cm to the right and 3cm down (down because the gradient is minus) and complete the triangle. Then draw in the line. Try to draw it so that for every 1cm the line goes to the right it goes down 3cm.

If you want to draw in a lot of triangles for each line that is fine. Or you may prefer not to draw any triangles at all, but just to use the lines on the page.

Draw the following lines by completing the triangles. Use the same graph page as above:

c $y = -2x - 10$ **d** $y = x + 8$ **e** $y = -x - 8$

f $y = \frac{1}{2}x + 4$ **g** $y = 3x + 8$ **h** $y = -4x$

☞

i Write down the equation of the lines a, b, c, d shown below:

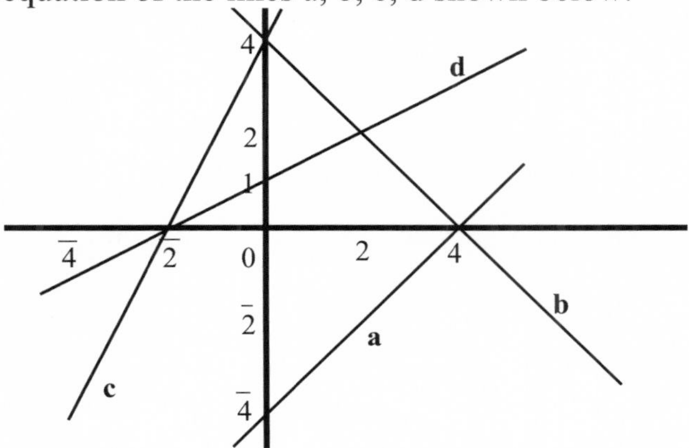

ALTERNATIVE METHOD USING SUBSTITUTION

We used substitution (the Sutra for this is *Specific and General)* earlier in this chapter for drawing graphs.

If we want to draw the graph of <u>$y = 2x - 3$</u> we choose a value for x, say $x = 2$, and find the corresponding y-value.

If $x = 2$ then $y = 2\times2 - 3 = 1$, and this gives the point (2,1) which we can plot.

Similarly if $x = 3$ then $y = 3$,
if $x = 4$ then $y = 5$,
if $x = 100$ then $y = 197$,
if $x = 0$ then $y = -3$,
if $x = \bar{2}$ then $y = \bar{7}$.

❋ Check these results yourself.
(Note that even if x is equal to a fraction or a decimal number we can find still y).

EXERCISE 6

Draw up a new graph with axes the same as the last one.

a Plot the points (2,1), (3,3), (4,5), $(0, \bar{3})$, $(\overline{2,7})$ found above and draw the line through them.

Check that the previous method of completing the triangle gives the same graph.

As before, plotting two points is enough to draw in the line, with one extra as a check.

Draw the following lines using the method of substitution:

b $y = 2x + 5$ **c** $y = \frac{1}{2}x + 9$ **d** $y = -x - 3$ **e** $y = 1 - x$ **f** $y = 3x + 9$

If an equation does not have y as the subject it can easily be rearranged to make y the subject.
For example $2x + y = 3$ can be rearranged to $y = -2x + 3$. Rearrange the next two equations to make y the subject before substituting and drawing the line.

g $y + \frac{1}{2}x = 1$ **h** $y + 2x + 11 = 0$

i Write down the coordinates of the point where

i $y = 2x+5$ meets $y = 3x+9$

ii $y = -x-3$ meets $y+2x+11=0$

iii $y+\frac{1}{2}x = 1$ meets $y = 1-x$

iv $y = 2x+5$ meets $y+\frac{1}{2}x = 1$.

If a point lies on a line then if the values of x and y are substituted into the equation of the line the two sides will be equal.
And if, after substituting, the two sides are not equal then the point is not on the line.

For example the point (4,5) is on the line $y = 2x - 3$ because $5 = 2\times4 - 3$.
Similarly the point (–2,3) is not on the line $y = 7 - 2x$ because $3 \neq 7 - -4$.

EXERCISE 7

Write down those points out of the four points given which are on the given line:

a $y = 3x + 5$ (4,17) (1,6) (–3, –4) (0,5)

b $2x + 3y = 8$ (1,2) (4,0) (0,1) (–2,4)

"From the intrinsic evidence of his creation, the Great Architect of the Universe now begins to appear as a pure mathematician."

Sir James Jeans (1877–1946)

ASTRONOMER AND MATHEMATICIAN

18

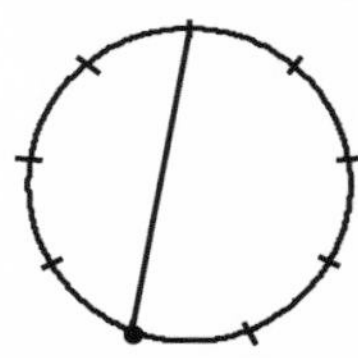

CHARTS

In this chapter we will look at how information can be obtained, how it can be shown on a graph or chart and how it can be abbreviated.

FREQUENCY TABLES

Susan has done a survey in her class to find out about shoe sizes.
First she drew up a table like this:

shoe size	tally	frequency
2		
3		
4		
5		
6		

Then she asked every one in her class what their shoe size was and filled in the table:

shoe size	tally	frequency
2	||	2
3	||||	4
4	~~||||~~ |	6
5	~~||||~~ ~~||||~~	10
6	~~||||~~ |||	8
		TOTAL= 30

Each time she asked a member of the class their shoe size she drew a vertical line in the **tally** column. When there are 4 marks and another one is to be added this is done by crossing out the 4 lines as you can see above. This makes it easy to count the total at the end because they make sets of 5.

Susan put the totals for each shoe size in the third column when she had finished the survey.
These numbers are called **frequencies**.

Finally she added up the frequencies and got 30. She then checked that there were 30 children in the class so that she had not missed anyone.

DOT DIAGRAMS AND LINE CHARTS

If information like that in the frequency table is displayed in a chart or diagram the information can be understood more easily *by mere observation*.

One way of doing this is with a dot diagram or a line chart:

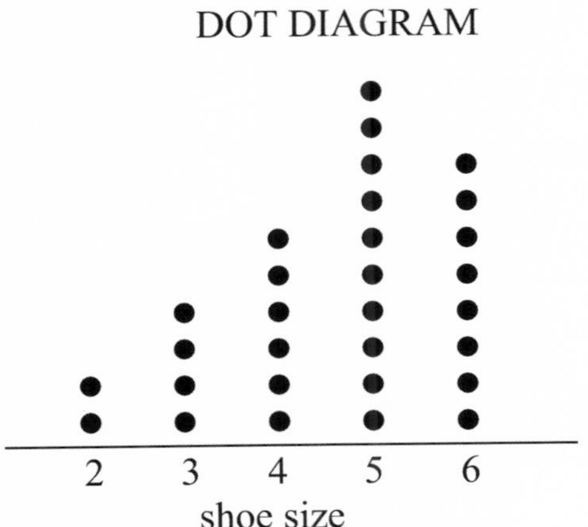

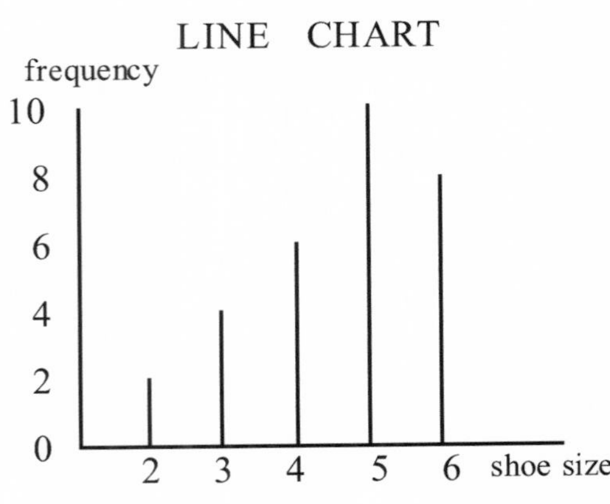

Look carefully at these two charts and see how the information is represented.

The Dot Diagram has one axis only and dots are placed in the appropriate place for each person in the class.

The Line Graph has two axes and the vertical axis is always the frequency axis. Lines are drawn whose length shows the frequency.

The axes are always clearly labelled in these charts and it is usual to give a clear, brief title.

1 Carry out a survey of your own.

You can choose: shoe sizes,
family sizes,
favourite fruits,
colours of cars,
the number of people in cars going past,
measuring handspans (to the nearest centimetre or half cm),
number of letters in surnames
or something else which your teacher says is appropriate.

Record your results in a Frequency Table.

Draw a Dot Diagram and also a Line Graph to show your results.
Keep your results safe, you may need them again later.

BAR CHARTS

These are also easy to draw. It is like a line graph but we draw a rectangular bar instead of a line, for the frequency.
Below is a bar chart for the shoe size survey from the beginning of this chapter.

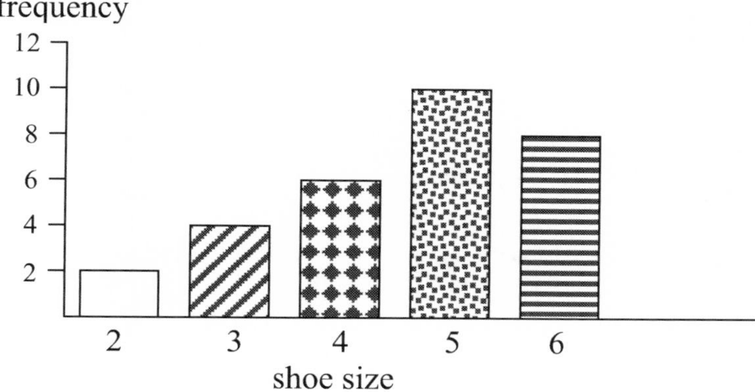

Note that the bars are of equal width.
Sometimes there is no gap between the bars.

❋ Use the information which you collected for your survey to draw a bar chart. Use a ruler, label the axes and put a title at the top. Use different colours for the bars.

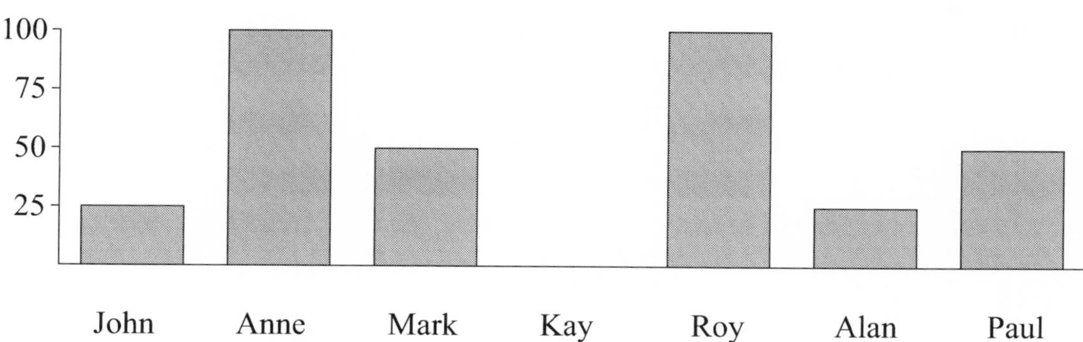

The bar chart above shows the distances a group of small children can swim in metres.

2 Who can swim the farthest?
3 How many can swim 50m?
4 Who cannot swim?

PICTOGRAMS

This is yet another way of displaying data. The diagram below, a **pictogram**, shows colour preferences for a number of people.
As you can see from the **key** each symbol represents 50 people so, for example, 100 people liked white best.
You will also see a half symbol on the line for blue. This means 25 people so 475 people liked blue.

Note that this graph is different to the others because the frequency is now along the horizontal axis rather than the vertical axis.

Sometimes matchstick men or some other symbol is used instead of faces. You can use any symbol you like.

5 Represent the information from your survey in a pictogram.

AVERAGES AND SPREAD

Information (data) like you obtained from your survey is frequently available for all sorts of subjects. There are huge amounts of data available and many ways of analysing it.

Apart from drawing graphs or charts of data we can make calculations with the numbers themselves. We can get an average (or typical) value and we can get an idea how much the data is spread out around that average value.

There are three important types of average: the **mode**, the **median** and the **mean**.

The **mode** of a collection of values is the one that occurs most often.
For example for the shoe size data we had more shoes of size 5 than any other size, so we say the mode is 5.

Sometimes there is more than one mode, or there may not be a mode at all.

EXAMPLE 1

Find the mode of **4 5 5 5 7 7 8 9 13**

There are more 5's than any other number so the modal value is 5.

The **median** is the middle value when they are placed in order.
In Example 1 the 9 numbers are already in order and the middle value is 7: the median is 7.

In the shoe size survey there were 30 people. The Dot Diagram shown earlier shows the 30 people in order. But since there are an even number of people there will not be a middle person, there will be two people in the middle.

You will find that in this example both the middle people are in the size 5 group, so we say the median is 5.

If the two middle values were different we would find the number which is in the middle between them (which is the mean of the two numbers).

The **mean** of a set of numbers is found by adding them all up and dividing the result by the number of numbers.
In Example 1 there are 9 numbers and they add up to 63. So we find $\frac{63}{9}$ which is 7.

So the mean is 7.

If the numbers in Example 1 were numbers of apples then finding the mean is like sharing out the apples equally between 9 people. There are 63 apples so everyone would get 7 apples.
The mean is the number we get if we share the numbers out equally.

Because an average is a specific value representing a collection of values this comes under the *Specific and General* formula.

The **spread** of a set of values is represented by the **range** which is the largest value minus the smallest value.

In Example 1 the range is 13–4 = 9. The bigger this number is, the more spread out the values are. If it is small then the values are packed closely together.
The range for the shoe sizes is 6–2 = 4 as the largest shoe size is 6 and the smallest is 2.
The range is found using *Only the Last Terms:* the last term minus the first term.

Here is a summary of the three averages and the spread.

The **mode** is the value that occurs most often.
The **median** is the middle value when they are in order.
The **mean** is found by adding the values and dividing by the number of numbers.

The **range** is the largest value minus the smallest value.

EXAMPLE 2

Find the mode, median and mean and range for:

11 8 5 11 13 12 10 8 9 11

The mode is 11 as there are more of these than any other number.

For the median we put the numbers into order first:
5 8 8 9 10 11 11 11 12 13. Then we see that there are two middle values, 10 and 11. So the median value is the mean of 10 and 11. This is $\frac{10+11}{2}$ which is 10.5, so the median value is 10.5. ☞

For the mean, we add the numbers to get a total of 98. Since there are 10 numbers we divide this by 10: $\frac{98}{10} = 9.8$. So the mean is 9.8.

The largest value is 13 and the smallest is 5, so the range is 8.

EXERCISE 1

Find the mode, median, mean and range for the following sets of data:

a 1 2 3 4 5 13 8 10 2 6 5 3 3

b 35 37 30 41 20 35

c 10.9 10.5 10.3 10.9 10.8

d 18 6 104 2 93 77

FRACTALS

We often find in nature that large structures are repeated on a smaller scale. A tree for example may divide its trunk into two parts. These may again each divide into two and so on down to the smallest twigs.

This could be modelled as follows:

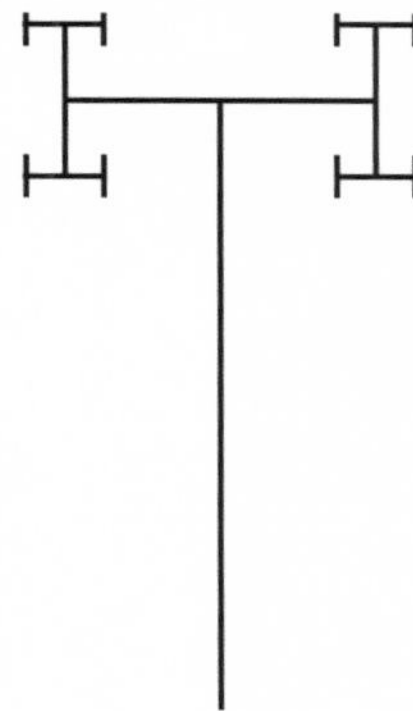

We start with a vertical "trunk" which divides into two. Then each part divides into two and so on. The diagram stops after 4 divisions but these may go on indefinitely.
This is a geometrical application of the *Proportionately* Sutra together with *By One More than the One Before.*

A figure in which a design is repeated on a smaller and smaller scale is called a **fractal**.
You will have met such things before in the chapter on Spirals.

A Take a sheet of graph paper and with the longer edge at the bottom mark a point near the bottom but in the middle. This point is the bottom point of the diagram shown below. Copy the symmetrical diagram, all numbers represent centimetres.

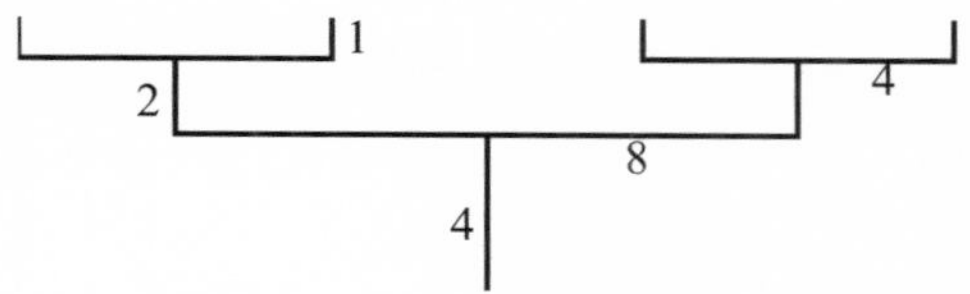

Notice that all horizontal distances are halved when they are drawn in the next level up and all vertical distances are similarly halved.

❋ Continue the drawing to include two more layers, each layer being half the size of the layer below.

B Coastlines also show this fractal property. A coastline appears erratic from a great distance but when looked at closer although less may be in view more detail is visible so the appearance is still erratic.

We can model this as follows:

❋ Draw a horizontal line, in pencil, 16cm long above your previous drawing: you will need 5cm above and below this line.

Divide this line into four equal parts and draw, in pencil, a square above the 2nd part and a square below the 3rd part as shown below.

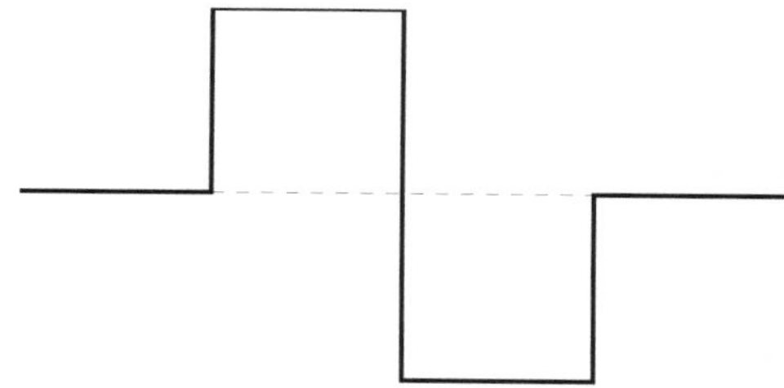

❋ Then rub out the middle two quarters of the line as shown by the dashed line above.

We now have 8 lines each a quarter of the original length.
The procedure applied to the original line is now applied to each of these 8 shorter lines.

❋ Divide the line on the left into quarters, draw the square above the 2nd quarter and below the 3rd quarter and rub out the middle two quarters of the line.

❋ Do this also for the other 7 lines.

❋ If possible repeat the whole procedure on each of the smaller lines.

❋ When you have finished go over your diagram in a colour.

C Take a sheet of triangular spotty paper and draw an equilateral triangle, in pencil, with sides 18cm.

❋ Divide each side into 3 equal parts and draw an equilateral triangle standing on the middle part of each side and pointing outwards (you may not be able to draw one of the triangles completely). Rub out the middle third of each side.

You should now have a star with 12 sides.

❋ Divide each of these 12 sides similarly into 3 equal parts, construct an equilateral triangle in the middle of each and rub out the middle third of the line.

❋ Repeat this one more time with the resulting shape, You will need to use ruler and compasses for this.

❋ When you have finished go over the shape (called the Koch Snowflake) in a colour.

"what are these wonderful numbers about which you are reasoning, in which, as you say, there is a unity such as you demand, and each unit is equal, invariable, indivisible, . . ."

Plato (429–347)

GREEK PHILOSOPHER

19

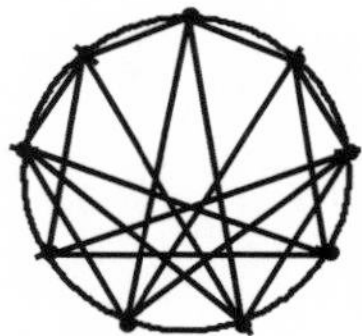

DIVISIBILITY

Write down any 3-figure number you like and then repeat the number so that you have a 6-figure number. So if you chose 328 you would write 328328.

Your 6-figure number, whatever it was, is divisible by 7.

❋ Check this by dividing your number by 7.

In the next chapter you will be able to see why this always happens.

We already know how to test for divisibility by 2, 3, 4, 5, 6, 9, 10, 15.
The tests we use are summarised below.

number	test
2	Is the last figure 0 or even?
3	Is the digit sum 3, 6 or 9?
4	Does 4 divide into the last two figures?
5	Is the last figure 5 or 0?
6	Is the numbers divisible by both 2 and 3?
9	Is the digit sum 9?
10	Is the last figure 0?
15	Is the number divisible by both 3 and 5?

EXAMPLE 1

Which of the above numbers divide into 70134?

Going through the tests above we see that 70134 is divisible by 2, 3 and 6 only.

❋ Check that you agree with this answer.

EXERCISE 1

Which of the numbers in the above list divide into:

a 38015 **b** 7770 **c** 123456 **d** 654321

DIVISIBILITY BY 8

A number is divisible by 8 if the last three figures are divisible by 8.

EXAMPLE 2

Is 70134 divisible by 8?

We divide 8 into the last three figures, 134: $8\underline{)\,1\ \ 3\ {}^{5}4}$
$\quad 1\ \ 6\ \text{r}\,6$

We find that 8 does not divide exactly so <u>70134 is not divisible by 8</u>.

1 Which of the numbers in Exercise 1 is/are divisible by 8?

When testing for divisibility by 8 it is worth testing for divisibility by 2 and 4 first because if a number is divisible by 8 it must also be divisible by 2 and by 4.
So there is no need to divide a number like 38015 by 8 as it ends in a 5 and so is not divisible by 2, and therefore cannot be divisible by 8 (or 4).
Similarly 87654 is divisible by 2 but not by 4, so it will not be divisible by 8.

EXERCISE 2

Test for divisibility by 8:

a 2447 **b** 64546 **c** 30208 **d** 554433

e 9182 **f** 453260 **g** 66688 **h** 777676

HIGHER DIVISORS

EXAMPLE 3

Is 4662 divisible by 18?

Since **18 = 2×9** a number will be divisible by 18 if it divisible by both 2 and 9. You can easily confirm that 4662 is divisible by 2 and 9 and that it is therefore divisible by 18.

Since 18 = 3×6 also you may think that we can test for 3 and 6 when testing for 18, but this does not work. Because 3 and 6 have a common factor of 3 you would be testing for divisibility by 3 twice, and not testing that the number is divisible by 9.

We choose 2×9 rather than 3×6 because 2 and 9 are **relatively prime**.

When testing for divisibility by higher divisors write the number as a product of factors which are **relatively prime.**

EXAMPLE 4

Is 1848 divisible by 24?

24 = 4×6 but we do not use 4 and 6 as they are not relatively prime.
24 = 3×8 is all right as 3 and 8 are relatively prime.
We find that 1848 is divisible by both 3 and 8 so it divisible by 24.

EXERCISE 3

Test the following for divisibility by the number in brackets:

a 3444 [12]	**b** 30258 [18]	**c** 126210 [30]	**d** 2772 [36]
e 7667 [36]	**f** 31815 [45]	**g** 2328 [24]	**h** 48888 [72]
i 12332 [24]	**j** 88884 [72]	**k** 7341 [52]	

BY ADDITION AND BY SUBTRACTION

In the sequence 7 14 21 28 35 . . . . which are just multiples of 7,

the numbers are all clearly divisible by 7. In fact since the sequence goes on forever it contains all the multiples of 7.

❋ Do you think that if you add 7 to any one of these numbers it will still be a multiple of 7?

❋ If you subtract 7 from any of them, will it still be a multiple of 7?

❋ If you add or subtract 14 or 21, will it still be a multiple of 7?

The answer to all these questions is Yes. If you add or subtract 7 or any multiple of 7 to or from the numbers in the above sequence they will still be divisible by 7.

Now consider the numbers **not** in the sequence 7 14 21 28 35 . . . .

❋ If you add 7 to a number not in this sequence, can it become a multiple of 7.

The answer is No. If you take the number 8 for example (which is not in the sequence) adding or subtracting 7, or any multiple of 7, will not make it divisible by 7.

> Adding or subtracting multiples of 7 to or from a number does not affect the divisibility or non-divisibility of that number by 7.

 **EXAMPLE 5**

Is 693 divisible by 7?

We could divide 693 to find out if there is a remainder.
But we may also notice that if we add 7 to 693 we get 700, which is clearly a multiple of 7.
So 693 is divisible by 7.

 **EXAMPLE 6**

Is 135 divisible by 7?

135 is close to 140, which is a multiple of 7, but if we add 7 to it we get 142.
So the answer to the question is No.

 **EXAMPLE 7**

Is 2817 divisible by 7?

Here we spot that that 28 is a multiple of 7 so remove it (we are in fact subtracting 2800 from the number).
This leaves 17 which is clearly not divisible by 7, so the answer is No.

This method does not apply only to divisibility by 7: it applies for any number.

The divisibility or non-divisibility of a number by a number n, is not affected by adding or subtracting multiples of n from the number.

 **EXAMPLE 8**

Is 117 divisible by 13?

Here we can add or subtract 13 (or multiples of it) to or from 117.

We see that if we add 13 to 117 we get 130 which is clearly a multiple of 13.
So we answer Yes.

EXAMPLE 9

Is 324 divisible by 8?

Here we can add or subtract 8's.
We notice that the 32 in 324 is a multiple of 8, so we can remove it.
This gives 4, which is not divisible by 8, so we say No.

EXAMPLE 10

Is 496 divisible by 14?

Since $14 = 2 \times 7$ we have to test for both 2 and 7.
2 clearly divides into 496.
In testing for 7 we spot that 49 is a multiple of 7 and removing it leaves 6 which is not divisible by 7.
So 496 is not divisible by 7 or 14.

EXERCISE 4

Test the following numbers for divisibility by the number in brackets:

a 203 [7]	**b** 232 [8]	**c** 274 [8]	**d** 792 [8]	**e** 215 [7]
f 426 [6]	**g** 217 [7]	**h** 1718 [17]	**i** 6424 [6]	**j** 6543 [13]
k 3331 [11]	**l** 153 [17]	**m** 1794 [6]	**n** 638 [14]	**o** 492 [8]

CANCELLING ZEROS

Look again at the sequence 7 14 21 28 35 . . . .

Divisibility or non-divisibility is not affected by adding zeros: 70, 1400 etc. are also divisible by 7.
Similarly, for numbers not in this sequence, they will not come into the sequence by adding zeros. For example 8 is not in the sequence and so 80 cannot be either, because you have only multiplied 8 by 10 so it still cannot contain a factor of 7.

> We can cancel off any zeros at the end of a number when testing for divisibility (provided we are not testing for divisibility by a number containing 2 or 5 as a factor)

EXAMPLE 11

Is 4200 divisible by 7?

We can ignore the zeros and ask if 7 divides into 42.
It does, so we say Yes.

EXAMPLE 12

Is 9088 divisible by 11?

We know we can subtract the 88 from 9088, giving 9000.
We then drop the zeros which leaves 9, which is not divisible by 11.
So 9088 is not divisible by 11.

EXAMPLE 13

Is 170014 divisible by 7?

Subtracting 14 leaves 170000.
Drop the zeros leaves 17 which is not divisible by 7.
170014 is therefore not divisible by 7.

EXERCISE 5

Test the following for divisibility by the number in brackets:

a 4000 [7] **b** 700 [11] **c** 90000 [17] **d** 2600 [13] **e** 907 [7]

f 80014 [7] **g** 21039 [13] **h** 340051 [17] **i** 8056 [7] **j** 680046 [23]

k 126009 [9] **l** 38019 [19] **m** 90707 [7] **n** 117001809 [9]

Note that we should only cancel zeros when the number we are testing for does not contain a factor of 2 or 5.

DIVISIBILITY BY 11

Testing for divisibility by 11 is particularly easy and comes under the formula *By Addition and by Subtraction*.

EXAMPLE 14

Is 7282231 divisible by 11?

We add all the digits in the odd positions and all the digits in the even positions and subtract the smaller result from the larger result.
If we end up with 0 or 11 or any multiple of 11 then the number is divisible by 11.

in the odd positions: 7+8+2+1 = 18

in the even positions: 2+2+3 = 7

Since here 18 – 7 = 11 the number **7282231 is divisible by 11**

EXERCISE 6

Test the following numbers for divisibility by the number in square brackets:

a 5192 [11] **b** 3476 [11] **c** 1358016 [11]

d 85547 [11] **e** 570317 [11] **f** 1030607 [11]

g 54373 [22] **h** 3564 [22] **i** 748 [44]

j 76362 [33] **k** 43731 [55]

l What should the 7 at the end of 1030607 be changed to, for the number to be divisible by 11?

Zerah Colburn (1804–1840) was asked, when he was eight, to raise the number 8 to the sixteenth power: he announced the answer (281,474,976,710,656) "promptly and with facility", causing the academic audience to weep. He was next asked to raise the numbers 2, 3, . . . 9 to the tenth power: and he gave the answers so rapidly that the gentleman who was taking them down was obliged to ask him to repeat them more slowly.

20

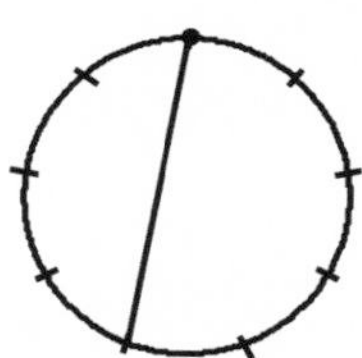

FURTHER MULTIPLICATION

We are familiar with the *Vertically and Crosswise* method for multiplying 2-figure numbers together and in this chapter we will see how to extend this pattern so that we can multiply numbers of any size in one line.

We will also meet some of the special numbers which are extremely useful in many areas of mathematics.
First let us revise multiplication of 2-figure numbers.

EXERCISE 1

Multiply the following:

a	**b**	**c**	**d**	**e**	**f**
3 1	2 3	5 2	1 7	4 4	8 2
5 1	3 2	4 6	6 1	5 4	2 8
____	____	____	____	____	____

MULTIPLYING 3-FIGURE NUMBERS

EXAMPLE 1

Find 504 × 321.

```
  5 0 4
  3 2 1
161784
```

The extended pattern for multiplying 3-figure numbers is as follows.

A Vertically on the left, 5×3 = **15**.

```
5 0 4
|
3 2 1
15
```

B Then crosswise on the left,
5×2 + 0×3 = 10.
Combining the 15 and 10:
15,10 = **160**.

```
5 0 4
 ×
3 2 1
160
```

C Next we take 3 products and add them up,
5×1 + 0×2 + 4×3 = 17. And 160,17 = **1617**.

(actually we are gathering up the hundreds by multiplying hundreds by units, tens by tens and units by hundreds)

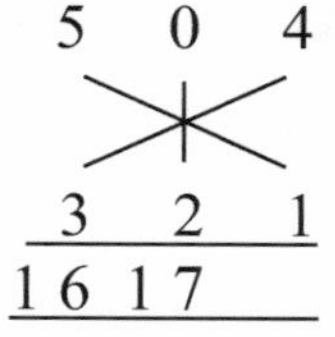

D Next we multiply crosswise on the right,
0×1 + 4×2 = 8: 1617,8 = **16178**.

```
5 0 4
   ×
3 2 1
16178
```

E Finally, vertically on the right,
4×1 = 4: 16178,4 = **161784**.

```
5 0 4
    |
3 2 1
161784
```

Note the symmetry in the 5 steps:
first there is 1 product, then 2, then 3, then 2, then 1.

We may summarise these steps as shown below:

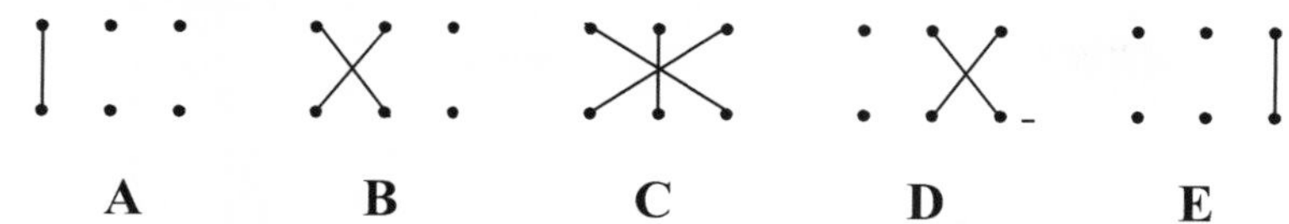

EXAMPLE 2

```
 3 2 1
 3 2 1 ×
103041
```

The 5 results are 9,12,10,4,1.
The mental steps are 9

9,12 = 102

102,10 = 1030

1030,4,1 = 103041

EXAMPLE 3

Find 123 × 45.

This can be done with the moving multiplier method or by the smaller vertical and crosswise pattern, treating 12 in 123 as a single digit .
Alternatively, we can put 045 for 45 and use the extended vertical and crosswise pattern:

```
1 2 3
0 4 5
5535
```

For the 5 steps we get 0,4,13,22,15.
Mentally we think 4; 53; 552; 5535.

EXERCISE 2

Multiply (there are no carries in the first few sums):

a	b	c	d	e	f
1 2 1	1 3 1	1 2 1	3 1 3	2 1 2	1 2 3
1 3 1	2 1 2	2 2 2	1 2 1	3 1 3	3 2 1
____	____	____	____	____	____

☞

g 212	**h** 222	**i** 246	**j** 105	**k** 106	**l** 515
414	333	333	507	222	555
m 444	**n** 321	**o** 123	**p** 124	**q** 137	**r** 131
777	321	271	356	803	771

FROM RIGHT TO LEFT

We can also calculate from right to left if we prefer, though for mental calculations left to right is much better.

EXAMPLE 4

```
    2 3 4
    2 3 4
  -------
  5 4 7 5 6
  1 2 2 1
```

We simply do the same operations but start at the right side:
4×4 = 16, put down 6 and carry 1 to the left.
3×4 + 4×3 = 24, 24 + carried 1 = 25, put down 5 and carry 2.
And so on.

EXERCISE 3

Multiply the following from right to left:

a 444 × 333 **b** 543 × 345 **c** 707 × 333 **d** 623 × 632

4-FIGURE NUMBERS

Once the vertical and crosswise method is understood it can be extended to multiply numbers of any size. We here extend the pattern one stage further, and multiply two 4-figure numbers.

EXAMPLE 5

```
   3  2  0  1
   4  3  0  2  ×
 1 3 7 7 0 7 0 2
```

The 7 steps are illustrated as follows:

A B C D E F G

Working from left to right we get:

A. $3 \times 4 = 12$
B. $3 \times 3 + 2 \times 4 = 17$
C. $3 \times 0 + 2 \times 3 + 0 \times 4 = 6$
D. $3 \times 2 + 2 \times 0 + 0 \times 3 + 1 \times 4 = 10$
E. $2 \times 2 + 0 \times 0 + 1 \times 3 = 7$
F. $0 \times 2 + 1 \times 0 = 0$
G. $1 \times 2 = 2$

The mental steps are therefore 12,17 = 137

137,6 = 1376

1376,10 = 13770

13770,7,0,2 = 13770702

Or calculating from right to left we get the numbers from G to A shown above:

```
   3  2  0  1
   4  3  0  2  ×
 1 3 7 7 0 7 0 2
   1   1
```

EXERCISE 4

Multiply the following from left to right or from right to left:

a 2 1 3 1
3 0 2 2

b 2 0 2 1
1 1 2 2

c 3 2 0 1
4 0 1 2

d 5 1 1 3
5 3 3 1

SQUARING

You will recall how we find the square of a 2-figure number by summing its duplexes from left to right.

EXAMPLE 6

$37^2 = \underline{1369}$.

The duplex of 3 = 3^2 = 9,
the duplex of 37 = 2×3×7 = 42,
the duplex of 7 = 7^2 = 49.

Summing these: $9,\underset{\smile}{4}2$ = 132, $13\underset{\smile}{2},49$ = 1369.

Practice a few of these to remind yourself of the method.

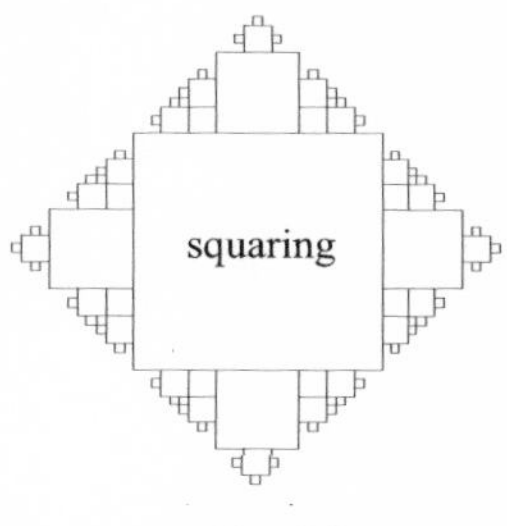

EXERCISE 5

Square:

a 62 **b** 71 **c** 26 **d** 34 **e** 56 **f** 83

We can also find the duplex of 3-figure numbers or bigger.

For 3 figures D is **twice the product of the outer pair + the square of the middle digit**, e.g. D(137) = 2×1×7 + 3^2 = **23**;

for 4 figures D is **twice the product of the outer pair + twice the product of the inner pair**, e.g. D(1034) = 2×1×4 + 2×0×3 = **8**;

D(10345) = 2×1×5 + 2×0×4 + 3^2 = **19**;

and so on.

EXERCISE 6

Find the duplex of the following numbers:

a 5 **b** 23 **c** 55 **d** 2 **e** 14

f 234 **g** 282 **h** 77 **i** 304 **j** 270

k 1234 **l** 3032 **m** 7130 **n** 20121 **o** 32104

As with 2-figure numbers the square of a number is just the total of its duplexes.

EXAMPLE 7

$341^2 = \underline{116281}$

Here we have a 3-figure number:

D(3) = 9, D(34) = 24, D(341) = 22, D(41) = 8, D(1) = 1.

Mentally:

9,24 = 114

114,22 = 1162

1162,8,1 = 116281

EXAMPLE 8

$4332^2 = \underline{18766224}$

D(4) = 16, D(43) = 24, D(433) = 33, D(4332) = 34,
D(332) = 21, D(32) = 12, D(2) = 4.

Mentally

16,24 = 184

184,33 = 1873

1873,34 = 18764

18764,21 = 187661

187661,12 = 1876622

1876622,4 = 18766224

EXERCISE 7

Square the following numbers:

a 212 **b** 131 **c** 204 **d** 513 **e** 263 **f** 264 **g** 313

h 217 **i** 3103 **j** 2132 **k** 1414 **l** 4144

m Find x given that $\mathbf{x23^2 = 388129}$

n Find b, c and d given that $\mathbf{b15^2 = 17cccd}$

SPECIAL NUMBERS

Some multiplications are particularly easy.

EXAMPLE 9

$23 \times 101 = \underline{2323}$

To multiply 23 by 101 we need 23 hundreds and 23 ones, which gives 2323.

The effect of multiplying any 2-figure by 101 is simply to make it repeat itself.

EXAMPLE 10

Similarly $69 \times 101 = \underline{6969}$

EXAMPLE 11

And $473 \times 1001 = \underline{473473}$

Here we have a 3-figure number multiplied by 1001 which makes the 3-figure number repeat itself.

EXAMPLE 12

$47 \times 1001 = \underline{47047}$

Here, because we want to multiply by 1001, we can think of 47 as 047. So we get 047047, or just 47047.

EXAMPLE 13

123 × 101 = 123,123 = <u>12423</u>

Here we have 12300 + 123 so the 1 has to be carried over.

EXAMPLE 14

28 × 10101 = <u>282828</u>

EXERCISE 8

Find:

a 46 × 101	**b** 246 × 1001	**c** 321 × 1001	**d** 439 × 1001
e 3456 × 10001	**f** 53 × 10101	**g** 74 × 1001	**h** 73 × 101
i 29 × 1010101	**j** 277 × 101	**k** 521 × 101	**l** 616 × 101

a special number

PROPORTIONATELY

EXAMPLE 15

43 × 201 = <u>8643</u>.

Here we bring in the *Proportionately* formula: because we want to multiply by 201 rather than 101 we must put twice 43 (which is 86) then 43.

EXAMPLE 16

31 × 10203 = <u>316293</u> we have 31×1, 31×2, 31×3.

EXERCISE 9

Find:

a 54 × 201 **b** 333 × 1003 **c** 41 × 10201 **d** 33 × 30201

e 17 × 20102 **f** 13 × 105 **g** 234 × 2001 **h** 234 × 1003

i 43 × 203

DISGUISES

Now it is possible for a sum to be of the above type without it being obvious: it may be disguised.

If we know the factors of some of these special numbers (like 1001, 203 etc.) we can make some sums very easy.

Suppose for example you know that **3 × 67 = 201**.

EXAMPLE 17

93 × 67 = <u>6231</u>.

Since 3 × 67 = 201,
therefore 93 × 67 = 31 × 3 × 67
= 31 × 201
= 6231

In other words, we recognise that one of the special numbers (201 in this case) is contained in the sum (as 3 × 67).

Now suppose we know that **3 × 37 = 111.**

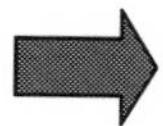

EXAMPLE 18

$24 \times 37 = \underline{888}$

We know that $3 \times 37 = 111$, which is a number very easy to multiply.

$$\begin{aligned} \text{So } 24 \times 37 &= 8 \times 3 \times 37 \\ &= 8 \times 111 \\ &= 888. \end{aligned}$$

Also $19 \times 21 = 399 = 40\bar{1}$.

EXAMPLE 19

$38 \times 63 = \underline{2394}$

Since $38 \times 63 = 2 \times 19 \times 3 \times 21 = 6 \times 19 \times 21 = 6 \times 40\bar{1} = 240\bar{6} = 2394$.

If we know the factors of these special numbers we can make good use of them when they come up in a sum, and they arise quite frequently.

Below is a list of a few of these numbers with their factors:

$67 \times 3 = 201$	**$17 \times 6 = 102$**	**$11 \times 9 = 10\bar{1}$**
$43 \times 7 = 301$	**$13 \times 8 = 104$**	**$19 \times 21 = 40\bar{1}$**
$7 \times 11 \times 13 = 1001$	**$29 \times 7 = 203$**	**$23 \times 13 = 30\bar{1}$**
$3 \times 37 = 111$	**$31 \times 13 = 403$**	**$27 \times 37 = 100\bar{1}$**

EXAMPLE 20

$62 \times 39 = \underline{2418}$

We see 31×13 contained in this sum:

$$\begin{aligned} 62 \times 39 &= 2\times31 \times 3\times13 \\ &= 2\times3 \times 31\times13 \\ &= 6 \times 403 \\ &= 2418 \end{aligned}$$

EXERCISE 10

Use the special numbers to find:

a 29 × 28	**b** 35 × 43	**c** 67 × 93	**d** 86 × 63
e 77 × 43	**f** 26 × 77	**g** 34 × 72	**h** 57 × 21
i 58 × 63	**j** 26 × 23	**k** 134 × 36	**l** 56 × 29
m 93 × 65	**n** 54 × 74	**o** 39 × 64	**p** 51 × 42

The special number 1001 explains how the trick shown at the beginning of the last chapter works.

Repeating the 3-figure number is equivalent to multiplying it by 1001, and since 7 divides into 1001, 7 will divide into the 6-figure number.

"I do not know what I may appear to the world; but to myself I seem to have been only like a boy playing on the seashore, and diverting myself in now and then finding a smoother pebble or a prettier shell than ordinary, whilst the great ocean of truth lay all undiscovered before me."

Sir Isaac Newton (1642–1726)

ENGLISH MATHEMATICIAN

21

COMBINING FRACTIONS

ADDITION AND SUBTRACTION

If the denominators of two fractions are the same it is very easy to add or subtract them.

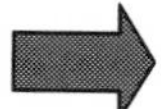

EXAMPLE 1

Find **a** $\frac{3}{7}+\frac{2}{7}$ **b** $2\frac{2}{5}+3\frac{4}{5}$

a Clearly three sevenths and two sevenths make five sevenths, or $\frac{3}{7}+\frac{2}{7}=\frac{5}{7}$.

b Similarly $2\frac{2}{5}+3\frac{4}{5}=5\frac{6}{5}$ we add the whole numbers and the fractions separately.

And since $\frac{6}{5}=1\frac{1}{5}$ this simplifies further to $6\frac{1}{5}$.

EXAMPLE 2

Find **a** $7\frac{8}{9} - 3\frac{2}{9}$ **b** $3\frac{4}{7} - \frac{6}{7}$.

a $7\frac{8}{9} - 3\frac{2}{9} = 4\frac{6}{9} = 4\frac{2}{3}$

We subtract the whole numbers, and subtract the numerators.

We can also cancel $\frac{6}{9}$ down to $\frac{2}{3}$.

b $3\frac{4}{7} - \frac{6}{7} = 2\frac{5}{7}$

Here we want to take $\frac{6}{7}$ from $\frac{4}{7}$ so we take away $\frac{4}{7}$ and we still have to take $\frac{2}{7}$ away so we take it from one of the 3 whole ones. This leaves only 2 whole ones and $\frac{5}{7}$ of the whole one from which we subtracted the $\frac{2}{7}$.

EXAMPLE 3

Find $4\frac{3}{4} - 7\frac{1}{4} + 8\frac{3}{4}$.

Where there are three or more fractions to combine we can combine the first two and then combine the answer with the third. But in this case, to avoid getting involved with minus numbers we may prefer to add up the first and third and then subtract the second:

So $4\frac{3}{4} + 8\frac{3}{4} = 12\frac{6}{4}$. Then $12\frac{6}{4} - 7\frac{1}{4} = 5\frac{5}{4} = 6\frac{1}{4}$.

EXERCISE 1

Add or subtract the following fractions, giving your answers as mixed numbers and cancelled down where possible:

a $\frac{2}{5} + \frac{2}{5}$ **b** $\frac{3}{8} + \frac{7}{8}$ **c** $\frac{5}{7} + \frac{5}{7}$ **d** $\frac{5}{6} + \frac{5}{6}$

e $3\frac{1}{5} + 4\frac{3}{5}$ **f** $5\frac{2}{3} + 2\frac{2}{3}$ **g** $4\frac{1}{3} + \frac{2}{3}$ **h** $\frac{3}{4} + 1\frac{1}{4} + 3\frac{1}{4}$

☞

i $\frac{10}{11}-\frac{4}{11}$ **j** $3\frac{5}{8}-1\frac{1}{8}$ **k** $7\frac{7}{10}-3\frac{6}{10}$ **l** $5\frac{4}{9}-\frac{6}{9}$

m $3\frac{1}{3}-1\frac{2}{3}$ **n** $8\frac{1}{15}-3\frac{4}{15}$ **o** $5-2\frac{2}{3}$ **p** $60-\frac{1}{5}$

q $1\frac{2}{5}+2\frac{4}{5}-1\frac{3}{5}$ **r** $3\frac{3}{7}+\frac{2}{7}-1\frac{6}{7}$ **s** $6\frac{1}{3}-3\frac{2}{3}+8\frac{1}{3}$ **t** $4-1\frac{3}{4}+3\frac{1}{4}$

u $8-1\frac{1}{6}-2\frac{1}{6}$ **v** $3-5\frac{1}{2}+9$ **w** $1-3\frac{4}{5}+10\frac{1}{5}$ **x** $1\frac{2}{3}+7\frac{1}{3}-2\frac{1}{3}+\frac{2}{3}$

EXAMPLE 4

Find $\frac{4}{9}+\frac{2}{3}$.

Here we see that the denominators are not the same. But 9 is a multiple of 3 and so we can multiply the top and bottom of $\frac{2}{3}$ by 3 to get $\frac{6}{9}$ which has the same denominator as $\frac{6}{9}$.

So $\frac{4}{9}+\frac{2}{3}=\frac{4}{9}+\frac{6}{9}=\frac{10}{9}$.

EXERCISE 2

Add the following (answers may be left top-heavy):

a $\frac{4}{5}+\frac{1}{10}$ **b** $\frac{1}{6}+\frac{1}{12}$ **c** $\frac{3}{4}+\frac{1}{8}$ **d** $\frac{1}{3}+\frac{5}{6}$ **e** $\frac{1}{3}+\frac{2}{9}$

f $\frac{7}{12}-\frac{1}{4}$ **g** $\frac{3}{20}+\frac{2}{5}$ **h** $1\frac{1}{5}+3\frac{1}{10}$ **i** $\frac{5}{6}-\frac{1}{3}$ **j** $3\frac{5}{8}-1\frac{1}{2}$

Where the denominators are the same all we need is *By Addition and By Subtraction* to do the addition or subtraction. Where one denominator is a multiple of the other as above we can use *Proportionately*. Otherwise we use *Vertically and Crosswise* as shown next.

EXAMPLE 5

Find **a** $\frac{2}{3}+\frac{1}{7}$ **b** $7\frac{4}{5}+2\frac{1}{3}$.

a We multiply crosswise and add to get the numerator:

$2\times7 + 1\times3 = 17,$

then multiply the denominators to get the denominator:

$3\times7 = 21.$

$\frac{2}{3} \times \frac{1}{7}$ $\qquad$ $\frac{2}{3} \quad \frac{1}{7}$

So $\frac{2}{3}+\frac{1}{7}=\frac{17}{21}$

The reason why this works is that in order to add the fractions we must get the denominators to be equal, and we do this by multiplying top and bottom of $\frac{2}{3}$ by 7 (to get a denominator of 21) and the top and bottom of $\frac{1}{7}$ by 3 (to get the same denominator of 21). So each numerator gets multiplied by the other denominator, which is exactly what we did.

b $7\frac{4}{5}+2\frac{1}{3}=9\frac{17}{15}=10\frac{2}{15}$ Here we can add the whole parts and the fractions separately: for the whole ones 7+2 = 9 and for the fractions:
$4\times3 + 1\times5 = 17$ = numerator,
and $5\times3 = 15$ = denominator.

EXAMPLE 6

Find **a** $\frac{6}{7}-\frac{1}{4}$ **b** $5\frac{4}{5}-1\frac{3}{4}$ **c** $4\frac{1}{3}-1\frac{2}{5}$.

a Subtraction is the same except we cross-multiply and **subtract** rather than add: $\frac{6}{7}-\frac{1}{4}=\frac{6\times4-1\times7}{7\times4}=\frac{17}{28}$

b $5\frac{4}{5}-1\frac{3}{4}=4\frac{4\times4-3\times5}{5\times4}=4\frac{1}{20}$ Similarly, but deal with the whole parts first.

c $4\frac{1}{3}-1\frac{2}{5}=3\frac{1\times5-2\times3}{3\times5}=3\frac{\bar{1}}{15}=2\frac{14}{15}$ Here we get a minus numerator, but it is easily dealt with by taking $\frac{1}{15}$ from one of the whole ones.

Alternatively, to avoid the minus number here, put both fractions into top-heavy form and subtract. This will mean dealing with larger numbers however.

EXERCISE 3

Combine the following, cancelling down your answer or leaving as mixed numbers where necessary:

a $\frac{2}{5}+\frac{1}{4}$ **b** $\frac{3}{8}+\frac{2}{5}$ **c** $\frac{1}{2}+\frac{2}{5}$ **d** $\frac{6}{7}+\frac{1}{2}$ **e** $\frac{4}{5}+\frac{2}{3}$

f $1\frac{1}{3}+2\frac{1}{4}$ **g** $3\frac{3}{4}+2\frac{1}{3}$ **h** $\frac{5}{6}+2\frac{1}{7}$ **i** $\frac{3}{4}+\frac{5}{6}$ **j** $5\frac{1}{2}+2\frac{3}{8}$

k $3\frac{4}{5}+1\frac{2}{3}$ **l** $1\frac{1}{5}+\frac{3}{10}$ **m** $\frac{3}{5}-\frac{2}{7}$ **n** $\frac{8}{9}-\frac{1}{2}$ **o** $\frac{3}{4}-\frac{1}{20}$

p $5\frac{3}{5}-2\frac{1}{2}$ **q** $10\frac{2}{3}-1\frac{2}{5}$ **r** $4\frac{1}{2}-1\frac{2}{3}$ **s** $5\frac{1}{10}-2\frac{1}{3}$ **t** $1\frac{3}{10}-\frac{2}{3}$

u $\frac{5}{12}+\frac{7}{18}$

COMPARING FRACTIONS

Some times we need to know whether one fraction is greater or smaller than another, or we may have to put fractions in order of size.

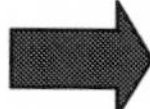

EXAMPLE 7

Put the fractions $\frac{4}{5}, \frac{2}{3}, \frac{5}{6}$ in ascending order.

Looking at the first two fractions we cross-multiply and subtract as if we wanted to subtract the fractions.
If we find the subtraction is possible without going into negative numbers then the first fraction must be greater: since 4×3 is greater than 2×5, $\frac{4}{5}$ must be greater than $\frac{2}{3}$. Doing this with $\frac{2}{3}$ and $\frac{5}{6}$ we find that 2×6 is less than 5×3, so $\frac{5}{6}$ is greater than $\frac{2}{3}$.
If we now cross-multiply $\frac{4}{5}$ with $\frac{5}{6}$ we find that $\frac{5}{6}$ is greater.

So in ascending order the fractions are: $\frac{2}{3}, \frac{4}{5}, \frac{5}{6}$.

EXERCISE 4

Put the following fractions in ascending order:

a $\frac{1}{3}, \frac{2}{5}$ **b** $\frac{3}{4}, \frac{8}{11}$ **c** $\frac{2}{3}, \frac{7}{12}, \frac{3}{4}$ **d** $\frac{5}{6}, \frac{5}{8}, \frac{6}{7}$

A SIMPLIFICATION

In the last question of Exercise 2 the numbers were rather large and some cancelling had to be done at the end. Where the denominators of two fractions are not relatively prime the working can be simplified as shown in the next example.

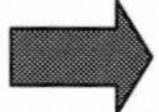

EXAMPLE 8

The denominators in $\frac{5}{12} + \frac{7}{18}$ are not relatively prime: there is a common factor of 6. We divide both denominators by this common factor and put these numbers below the denominators:

$$\frac{5}{\underset{(2)}{12}} + \frac{7}{\underset{(3)}{18}} = \frac{5\times3 + 7\times2}{12\times3} = \frac{29}{36}$$

So we put 2 and 3 below 12 and 18.
Then when cross-multiplying we use the 2 and 3 rather than the 12 and 18.
For the denominator of the answer we cross-multiply in the denominators: either 12×3 or 18×2, both give 36.

Subtraction of fractions with denominators which are not relatively prime is done in just the same way, except we subtract in the numerator as before.

EXERCISE 5

Use this simplification to add or subtract the following:

a $\frac{1}{3}+\frac{4}{9}$ **b** $\frac{3}{8}+\frac{1}{6}$ **c** $\frac{3}{5}+\frac{3}{10}$ **d** $\frac{5}{6}-\frac{3}{4}$ ☞

e $\frac{5}{6}+\frac{3}{4}$ **f** $\frac{5}{18}-\frac{1}{27}$ **g** $3\frac{3}{4}-1\frac{1}{8}$ **h** $\frac{7}{36}-\frac{11}{60}$

EXERCISE 6

Try the following problems involving fractions:

a How much less than 3 is the sum of $\frac{1}{3}$ and $\frac{1}{4}$?

b If I spend $\frac{1}{3}$ of the day sleeping and $\frac{5}{12}$ of the day working what fraction of the day is left, and how many hours is that?

c I spent $\frac{1}{3}$ of my money at the stationers and $\frac{5}{12}$ at the grocers and had £1.20 left. How much money did I have to begin with?

MULTIPLICATION AND DIVISION

EXAMPLE 9

Find **a** $\frac{1}{2}\times\frac{3}{4}$ **b** $1\frac{1}{4}\times2\frac{3}{5}$.

a $\frac{1}{2}\times\frac{3}{4}=\frac{1\times3}{2\times4}=\frac{3}{8}$ we simply multiply the numerators to get the numerator of the answer, and multiply the denominators to get the denominator of the answer.

We can verify this by showing that ½ of ¾ is $\frac{3}{8}$:

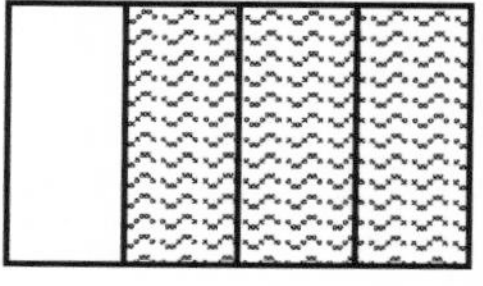

$\frac{3}{4}$

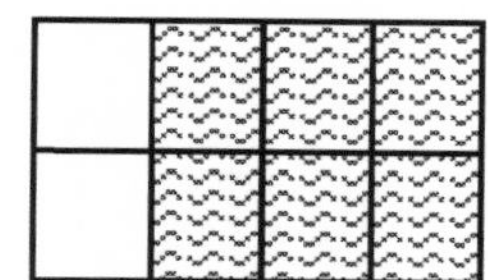

half of $\frac{3}{4}=\frac{3}{8}$

b $1\frac{1}{4}\times2\frac{3}{5}=\frac{5}{4}\times\frac{13}{5}=\frac{65}{20}=3\frac{5}{20}=3\frac{1}{4}$ Here we must change the mixed numbers into top-heavy fractions at the beginning, and then we can proceed as before.

EXAMPLE 10

Find **a** $\frac{3}{4} \div \frac{2}{5}$ **b** $1\frac{1}{2} \div \frac{1}{4}$.

a $\frac{3}{4} \div \frac{2}{5} = \frac{3 \times 5}{2 \times 4} = \frac{15}{8} = 1\frac{7}{8}$ We simply cross-multiply and put the first product over the second product.

In fact either answer, $\frac{15}{8}$ or $1\frac{7}{8}$, is acceptable depending on the wording of the question.

b $1\frac{1}{2} \div \frac{1}{4} = \frac{3}{2} \div \frac{1}{4} = \frac{12}{2} = 6$. As with multiplication we first change mixed numbers into top-heavy fractions.

We can verify this by showing that when 1½ is divided into ¼'s there are 6 of them:

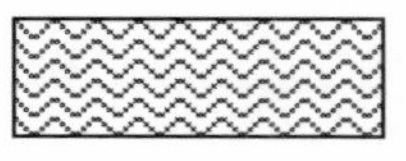

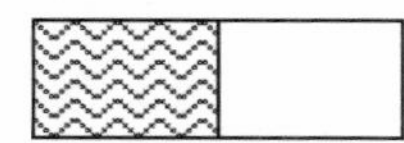

1½

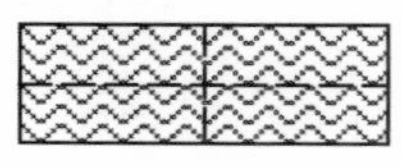

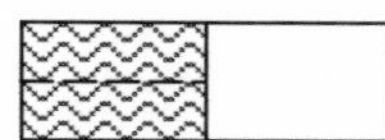

6 quarters in 1½

Since multiplication and division are opposite processes the above methods can also be verified as follows:

Example 9 shows that $\frac{1}{2} \times \frac{3}{4} = \frac{1 \times 3}{2 \times 4} = \frac{3}{8}$ so that $\frac{3}{8} \div \frac{3}{4}$ should be $\frac{1}{2}$.

But $\frac{3}{8} \div \frac{3}{4} = \frac{12}{24} = \frac{1}{2}$.

We have multiplied $\frac{1}{2}$ by $\frac{3}{4}$ and divided by $\frac{3}{4}$ which gives us our $\frac{1}{2}$ back.

EXERCISE 7

Multiply or divide leaving your answer **cancelled down and as top-heavy fractions** where appropriate:

a $\frac{2}{3}\times\frac{4}{5}$ **b** $\frac{6}{7}\times\frac{1}{11}$ **c** $\frac{2}{5}\times\frac{7}{8}$ **d** $\frac{3}{2}\times\frac{7}{9}$

e $2\frac{1}{3}\times3\frac{1}{2}$ **f** $3\frac{3}{4}\times1\frac{2}{3}$ **g** $4\frac{1}{4}\times\frac{2}{5}$ **h** $\frac{1}{6}\times1\frac{3}{10}$

i $\frac{2}{5}\div\frac{3}{7}$ **j** $\frac{7}{9}\div\frac{1}{3}$ **k** $\frac{1}{11}\div\frac{2}{11}$ **l** $\frac{3}{7}\div\frac{7}{3}$

m $3\frac{1}{3}\div3\frac{3}{4}$ **n** $3\frac{1}{4}\div1\frac{1}{7}$ **o** $\frac{5}{6}\div1\frac{1}{3}$ **p** $3\frac{1}{3}\div\frac{20}{3}$

A SIMPLIFYING DEVICE

In question **f** in the last exercise you will have had $\frac{15}{4}\times\frac{5}{3}$ and looking at the 15 and the 3 here, which are not relatively prime, we cancel by the common factor, 3, which gives $\frac{5}{4}\times\frac{5}{1}=\frac{25}{4}$

For multiplication we can cancel any number on top with any number on the bottom. And sometimes we can cancel both ways: e.g. $\frac{10}{21}\times\frac{9}{25}$ can be cancelled by 5 one way and by 3 the other way, giving $\frac{2}{7}\times\frac{3}{5}=\frac{6}{35}$.

Also, in question **m** we had $\frac{10}{3}\div\frac{15}{4}$. Here we can cancel the 10 and 15 to get $\frac{2}{3}\div\frac{3}{4}=\frac{8}{9}$.

For division we can cancel any two numbers which are either both on top or both on the bottom.

And we can sometimes cancel on the top and on the bottom: e.g. $\frac{6}{35}\div\frac{9}{14}$ can be cancelled by 3 on the top and by 7 on the bottom, giving $\frac{2}{5}\div\frac{3}{2}=\frac{4}{15}$.

EXERCISE 8

Use this cancelling down to find the following:

a $\frac{6}{5} \times \frac{1}{9}$ **b** $\frac{7}{12} \times \frac{8}{11}$ **c** $2\frac{2}{3} \times \frac{1}{12}$ **d** $\frac{10}{21} \times \frac{14}{15}$

e $\frac{8}{9} \div \frac{10}{7}$ **f** $\frac{6}{25} \div \frac{7}{15}$ **g** $\frac{6}{11} \div \frac{15}{22}$ **h** $1\frac{3}{7} \div 4\frac{2}{7}$

We can summarise the methods of adding, subtracting, multiplying and dividing fractions as follows:

Addition	**Subtraction**	**Multiplication**	**Division**
$\frac{4}{5} \times \frac{1}{3}$	$\frac{4}{5} \times \frac{1}{3}$	$\frac{4}{5} - \frac{1}{3}$	$\frac{4}{5} \times \frac{1}{3}$

EXERCISE 9

Try the following problems involving fractions:

a Find four fifths of twelve hundred.

b I have read $\frac{2}{3}$ of a book of 444 pages. How many pages have I left to read?

c The length of a room is 2½ times the height and the width is $\frac{3}{5}$ of the length. If the height of the room is 2.8m find the perimeter of the floor.

d Three sisters shared a cake. The eldest had $\frac{1}{3}$ of it and the next sister had $\frac{3}{4}$ of the remainder. What fraction of the cake was left for the third sister?

"...numbers (in Mathematics) labour under no such handicaps and disadvantages based on personal prejudices, partialities, hatreds etc. They are, on the contrary, strictly and purely impersonal and objective in their behaviour etc, follow the same rules uniformly and invariantly (with no question of outlook, approach, personal psychology involved therein) and are therefore absolutely reliable and dependable."

Bharati Krsna Tirthaji (1884–1960)

DISCOVERER OF VEDIC MATHEMATICS

22

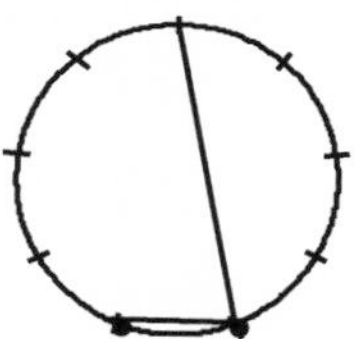

ARITHMETICAL OPERATIONS

Arithmetical Operations refers to the various ways in which numbers can be combined together.

Addition, subtraction, multiplication, division and squaring are all examples of arithmetical operations.

THE ORDER OF OPERATIONS

When we add or multiply the order is not important: $3 + 4$ is the same as $4 + 3$
and 3×4 is the same as 4×3.

For subtraction and division the order **is** important: $4 - 2$ is different from $2 - 4$
and $4 \div 2$ is different from $2 \div 4$.

Similarly when adding a series of numbers we can add in any order we like:
in adding $52 + 39 + 8$ we may prefer to add the 52 and 8 first and then the 39.

And in multiplying $2 \times 18 \times 5$ we may prefer to multiply 2 by 5 first and then multiply by 18.

In this section we are going to look at how to work out sums which contain a mixture of different operations.

✵ What is the value of $\mathbf{2 \times 3 + 4}$ and $\mathbf{2 + 3 \times 4}$?

In fact there is a convention (rule) that if there is a mixture of addition and multiplication then the **multiplication is always done first**.

So the answers to the sums above are 10 and 14 because in the second sum we first multiply 3 by 4 and then add on the 2 afterwards.

EXAMPLE 1

Find $3 \times 4 + 4 \times 5$.

We see two multiplications here: 3×4 and 4×5 and they must both be done before adding.

Since $3\times4=12$ and $4\times5=20$ the sum becomes $12 + 20$ which gives the answer <u>32</u>.

EXERCISE 1

Find the value of:

a $7 + 3 \times 5$ **b** $8 + 4 \times 6 + 3$ **c** $5 \times 9 + 3 \times 3$ **d** $19 + 88 \times 96$

e $9\times7+4\times7+7\times3$ **f** $4 + 3 \times 3 \times 7$ **g** $98 + 98 \times 98$ **h** $102\times103+104$

The convention referred to above is actually wider than stated:

All multiplications and divisions should be done before additions and subtractions.

EXAMPLE 2

Evaluate $50 - 8 \div 4 + 7$.

To find the value of this we must do the division first.
Since $8 \div 4 = 2$ the sum becomes $50 - 2 + 7$ which is <u>55</u>.

It does not matter what order we work out $50 - 2 + 7$, we get 55 any way.

EXAMPLE 3

Evaluate $18 \div 3 + 4 \times 5$.

Since $18 \div 3 = 6$, and $4 \times 5 = 20$ we get $18 \div 3 + 4 \times 5 = 6 + 20 = \underline{26}$.

EXERCISE 2

Evaluate the following:

a $12 + 8 \div 4$	**b** $80 - 6 \times 7$	**c** $21 \div 7 - 6 \div 3$	**d** $10 + 3 \times 5 - 4 \div 2$
e $100 - 50 \div 5$	**f** $3 + 4 \times 5 - 6 \div 2$	**g** $100 - 25 \times 5$	**h** $5 + 4 \div 2 - 1 \times 3$

TWO PUZZLES

Suppose you are given the 9 symbols: 1, 2, 3, 4, 5, +, –, ×, ÷ and you have to order them make a sum (like the last question in the last exercise).

- ❋ Which combination gives the largest possible answer?
- ❋ Can you also arrange the symbols to get 0?

BRACKETS

Let us go back to the sum $\mathbf{2 + 3 \times 4}$ (which equals 14).
If we wanted to indicate that the 2 + 3 must be worked out first this can be shown by putting it in brackets:

$$\mathbf{(2 + 3) \times 4 = 20}$$

Brackets are always worked out first.

The full convention is: work out **Brackets** first,
then **Multiplication and Division,**
then **Addition and Subtraction.**

EXAMPLE 4

Find $10 \times (15 - 8) + 3$.

We work out the bracket first: $10 \times (15 - 8) + 3 = 10 \times 7 + 3$
then multiply: $= 70 + 3$
then add: $= \underline{73}$.

EXAMPLE 5

Find $7 + 3(18 + 7) - 12 \div 3$.

You may recall that $3(18 + 7)$ means that the bracket is multiplied by 3.

Brackets first: $7 + 3(18 + 7) - 12 \div 3 = 7 + 3 \times 25 - 12 \div 3$
then $\times$ and $\div$: $= 7 + 75 - 4$
then $+$ and $-$: $= \underline{78}$.

EXAMPLE 6

Find $\frac{3(5+9)}{7}$.

Here the 3 is multiplying the bracket and the 7 is dividing the top of the fraction.

Again we work out the bracket first, then multiply.
This gives $\frac{42}{7} = \mathbf{6}$ as the answer.

EXAMPLE 7

Find $\frac{30+24}{45}$.

There is no bracket in this but the line of the fraction itself acts as a bracket so we always proceed as if there was a bracket on the top (or the bottom) line:

$$\frac{30+24}{45} = \frac{(30+24)}{45} = \frac{54}{45} = \frac{6}{5}.$$

EXERCISE 3

Evaluate:

a $100 - 3(21 - 9)$ **b** $8 + 2(3 + 4 - 5)$ **c** $5(3-1) - 4(2 + 3)$ **d** $2(80-37) - 48 \div 8$

e $\frac{3(8-3)}{20}$ **f** $\frac{5(20-9)}{11}$ **g** $7 + \frac{2(8-5)}{3}$ **h** $\frac{6(2+8)}{5(8-2)}$

i $\frac{7+15}{11}$ **j** $\frac{12}{2+1}$ **k** $\frac{17+13}{17-13}$ **l** $\frac{2(8-2)}{3(5+7)} + 1$

In the following exercise you are asked to insert brackets in the place which makes the sum correct.
So for example $2 \times 3 + 4 - 5 = 9$ is not correct.
But $2 \times (3 + 4) - 5 = 9$ is correct.

EXERCISE 4

Insert a pair of brackets to make the following correct:

a $5 + 4 \times 3 - 2 = 9$ **b** $3 + 4 - 5 \times 6 = 12$ **c** $7 \times 6 - 5 + 4 = 11$

d $2 + 3 \times 4 + 5 = 29$ **e** $5 \times 4 + 3 - 2 = 25$ **f** $8 \times 6 - 4 \div 2 = 8$

g $2 \times 4 + 6 - 8 = 12$ **h** $7 + 5 \div 3 + 1 = 5$ **i** $5 \times 4 + 3 - 2 = 33$

CANCELLING

EXAMPLE 8

Find $\frac{16 \times 63}{56}$

Rather than finding 16×63 and then dividing we can cancel any factor in the top with any common factor in the bottom.

Seeing the common factor of 7 in 63 and 56 we cancel it out to get $\frac{16 \times 9}{8}$. ☞

And we now see a common factor of 8 in the top and bottom which we also cancel out:

$\frac{2\times9}{1} = \underline{18}$.

EXAMPLE 9

Find $\frac{15\times27}{18\times24}$

Looking for common factors we see a common factor of 9 in 27 and 18, so we cancel this out: $\frac{15\times3}{2\times24}$.

Then we see that 3 and 24 have a common factor of 3 which gives: $\frac{15\times1}{2\times8}$

This gives $\frac{15}{16}$ as the final answer.

The cancelling could have been done in a different order here, but the answer will be just the same whichever order is chosen.

If we cancel 15 and 18 by 3 first we get $\frac{5\times27}{6\times24}$.

Then we could cancel 27 and 24 by 3: $\frac{5\times9}{6\times8}$.

And finally cancel 6 and 9 by 3: $\frac{5\times3}{2\times8}=\frac{15}{16}$ again.

It is best to cancel by the biggest factor we can find, and keep cancelling as far as possible.

EXERCISE 5

Simplify:

a $\frac{18\times21}{14\times27}$ **b** $\frac{30\times45}{25\times27}$ **c** $\frac{36\times50}{30}$ **d** $\frac{72}{40\times16}$

e $\frac{60\times33\times7}{42\times22}$ **f** $\frac{3\times54}{18\times20}$ **g** $\frac{18\times16}{22\times24}$ **h** $\frac{18\times70}{7\times15\times12}$

i compose a fraction of your own, with at least four different numbers, which cancels down to $\frac{1}{2}$.

SOME REVISION OF DECIMALS

The following exercise is revision of your earlier work on decimals.

EXERCISE 6

Evaluate the following:

a $58.34 + 1.8$ **b** $5.67 + 77.2 + 6$ **c** $88.8 - 3.4$ **d** $3.4516 - 0.222$

e $15 - 6.4$ **f** $1.2 + 80.9 - 1.03$ **g** 4.2×3 **h** 2.006×6

i $5.35 \div 5$ **j** $0.6 \div 5$ **k** $23.03 \div 7$ **l** 3.456×10

m 5.6×100 **n** 6.3×200 **o** $33.44 \div 10$ **p** $0.07 \div 100$

q $16.86 \div 20$

Convert to simple fractions: **r** 0.9 **s** 0.12 **t** 0.011 **u** 3.4

Convert to decimals: **v** $\frac{3}{10}$ **w** $\frac{7}{1000}$ **x** $\frac{19}{100}$ **y** $\frac{25}{10}$

Next we consider multiplying a decimal by a decimal and dividing a decimal by a decimal.

MULTIPLICATION OF DECIMALS

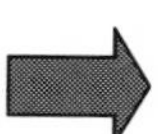

EXAMPLE 10

$0.3 \times 0.07 = \underline{0.021}$

Since $3 \times 7 = 21$, 21 must appear in the answer.
We have only to decide where the decimal point goes.

In terms of fractions the sum is $\frac{3}{10} \times \frac{7}{100}$ which equals $\frac{21}{1000}$.

Changing this back to a decimal we get 0.021.

Notice that in the sum $\underline{0.3 \times 0.07}$ there is a total of 3 figures after the decimal points. And in the answer $\underline{0.021}$ there are also 3 figures after the decimal point. In fact this is a general rule:

> In multiplying decimals there are as many figures after the decimal point in the answer as there are after the decimal points in the sum.

EXAMPLE 11

$0.2 \times 0.04 \times 1.2 = \underline{0.0096}$

We find 2×4×12, which is 96.
We count 4 figures after the decimal points in the sum (0.2×0.04×1.2) so there are to be 4 figures after the decimal point in the answer.
We therefore count back 4 places from the end of 96 which means we have to insert two zeros.
This gives us 0.0096 which has 4 figures after the point.

EXAMPLE 12

$21.5 \times 0.04 = \underline{0.86}$

Ignoring the points first of all: 215×4 = 860.
There are 3 figures after the points in the sum so we count back 3 spaces from the end of 860 to get 0.86.

Note that when we get the 860 we do not drop the 0 off immediately but count from the right-hand end of 860.

EXERCISE 7

Multiply the following:

a 0.7×0.8 **b** 0.2×0.3×0.04 **c** 0.007×0.09 **d** 3.3×0.4 **e** 80.8×0.9

f 2.7×2.3 **g** 3.5×0.02 **h** 3.003×0.7 **i** 0.1×0.01 **j** 0.6^2

k 4.5^2 **l** 0.4^3 **m** 3.2×4.3 **n** 0.44×5.6 **o** 5.4^2 **p** 0.34^2

We can use all our earlier multiplication methods on numbers with decimal points in them.
We just ignore the points first of all, do the multiplication and insert the point at the end.

EXAMPLE 13

Find 6.3 × 67.

We can use a special method to find 63 × 67 which gives 4221.
And the point goes one place in from the right: <u>422.1</u>.

EXERCISE 8

Multiply the following:

a 4.4 × 4.6　　**b** 35 × 3.5　　**c** 9.8 × 9.6　　**d** 9.7 × 97

e 10.3 × 108　　**f** 998 × 9.93　　**g** 2.3 × 3.3　　**h** 0.21 × 3.4

i 333 × 2.3　　**j** 3.14 × 25　　**k** 3.23 × 67.3　　**l** 43.21 × 4.1

DECIMAL DIVISION

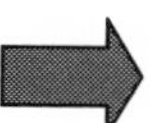

EXAMPLE 14

0.18 ÷ 0.003 = <u>60</u>.

If we write the sum as a fraction: $0.18 \div 0.003 = \frac{0.18}{0.003}$.

We can now make the denominator (bottom of the fraction) a whole number by multiplying the numerator and denominator both by 1000.

$$\frac{0.18}{0.003} = \frac{180}{3} = 60$$

We divide decimals by writing or thinking of the sum as a fraction, multiplying both numbers so that the denominator is a whole number and then dividing.

EXAMPLE 15

$1.82 \div 0.04 = \frac{182}{3} = \frac{91}{2} = \underline{45.5}$

Here we need to multiply both numbers by 100.

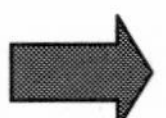

EXAMPLE 16

$\frac{1.6 \times 4.2}{2.4} = \frac{16 \times 42}{240} = \frac{16 \times 7}{40} = \frac{2 \times 7}{5} = \frac{14}{5} = \underline{2.8}$

Here we can multiply top and bottom by 100 as this gives us whole numbers and makes it easy to cancel (because we multiply 1.6 by 10 <u>and</u> 4.2 by 10 to get whole numbers).
Then we first cancel by 6 and then by 8.

EXERCISE 9

Find:

a $0.6 \div 0.02$ **b** $3.6 \div 0.009$ **c** $0.07 \div 0.1$ **d** $15 \div 0.03$

e $12.21 \div 0.3$ **f** $42 \div 0.6$ **g** $28.21 \div 0.07$ **h** $6.111 \div 0.9$

i $\frac{2.4 \times 3.9}{2.6}$ **j** $\frac{0.07 \times 0.8}{0.02}$ **k** $\frac{5.6 \times 0.12}{0.16}$ **l** $\frac{4.8}{0.6 \times 0.02}$

Ernst Kummer was a well-known German algebraist. Though he was brilliant at algebra his arithmetic was often rather poor. Apparently, during one lecture he had to find 9×7: "Right, 9×7, that's er... um...". One student, seeing his difficulty, suggested it was 61, which Kummer wrote on the board. Kummer was about to continue when another student said he thought it should be 69. Then Kummer said "Come, come gentlemen, it can't be both, it must be one or the other."

23

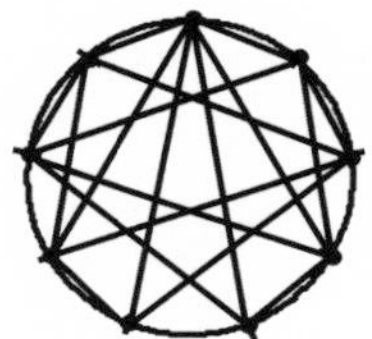

SPECIAL DIVISION

You may recall that it is very easy to divide by 9 in the Vedic system and this is because 9 is close to the base number 10.

EXAMPLE 1

Find 1234 ÷ 9.

$$\begin{array}{r} 9\overline{)\,1\ \ 2\ \ 3\ \ 4\ } \\ \underline{1\ \ 3\ \ 6\,r\,10} \end{array}$$

The answer is 136 remainder of 10, which becomes <u>137 remainder 1</u>.

EXERCISE 1

Divide the following numbers by 9:

a 222 **b** 602 **c** 37 **d** 2131 **e** 4040 **f** 444

EXAMPLE 2

Find 3172 ÷ 9.

$$9\overline{)3\quad 1\quad 7\quad 2}$$
$$\underline{3\quad 4\quad 11\ r\ 13}$$

Here we find we get an 11 and a 13: the first 1 in the 11 must be carried over to the 4, giving 351, and there is also another 1 in the remainder so we get <u>352 remainder 4</u>.

A SHORT CUT

However, to avoid the build-up of large numbers like 11 and 13 in this example we may notice, before we put the 4 down, that the next step will give a 2-figure number and so we put 5 down instead:

$$9\overline{)3\quad 1\quad 7\quad 2}$$
$$\underline{3\quad 5\quad 2\ r\ 4}$$

Then add 5 to 7 to get 12, but as the 1 has already been carried over we only put the 2 down. Finally, 2+2 = 4.

EXAMPLE 3

Find 777 ÷ 9.

$$9\overline{)7\quad 7\quad 7}$$
$$\underline{8\quad 6\ r\ 3}$$

If we put 7 for the first figure we get 14 at the next step, so we put 8.
8+7 = 15 the 1 has already been carried over but if we put the 5 down we see a 2-figure coming in the next step, so we put 6 down.
6+7 = 13 the 1 has been carried over, so just put down the 3.

EXERCISE 2

Divide the following by 9:

a 6153 **b** 3272 **c** 555 **d** 8252

e 661 **f** 4741 **g** 4747 **h** 2938

i 12345 **j** 75057 **k** 443322 **l** 1918161

It is similarly easy to divide by numbers near other base numbers: 100, 1000 etc.

EXAMPLE 4

Suppose we want to divide 235 by 88 (which is close to 100)

We need to know how many times 88 can be taken from 235 and what the remainder is.
Since every 100 must contain an 88 there are clearly 2 88's in 235.
And the remainder will be 2 12's (because 88 is 12 short of 100) plus the 35 in 235. So the answer is 2 remainder 59. (24+35=59)

A neat way of doing the division is as follows.

Set the sum out like this:

$$\begin{array}{r|l} 8\,8)2 & 3\,5 \\ \hline & \\ \hline \end{array}$$

We separate the two figures on the right because 88 is close to 100 (which has 2 zeros).

Then since 88 is 12 below 100 we put 12 below 88, as shown below.

$$\begin{array}{ccc|cc} \mathbf{8} & \mathbf{8}) & \mathbf{2} & \mathbf{3} & \mathbf{5} \\ {\scriptstyle 1} & {\scriptstyle 2} & & {\scriptstyle 2} & {\scriptstyle 4} \\ \hline & & \mathbf{2} & \mathbf{5} & \mathbf{9} \\ \hline \end{array}$$

We bring down the initial 2 into the answer.

This 2 then multiplies the flagged 12 and the 24 is placed under the 35 as shown.
We then simply add up the last 2 columns.

Note that the deficiency of 88 from 100 is given by the formula *All from 9 and the Last from 10.*

Note also that **the position of the vertical line is always determined by the number of noughts in the base number**: if the base number has 4 noughts then the vertical line goes 4 digits from the right, and so on.

EXAMPLE 5

Divide 31313 by 7887.

We set the sum out as before: **7 8 8 7) 3 | 1 3 1 3**

```
7 8 8 7 ) 3 | 1 3 1 3
2 1 1 3     | 6 3 3 9
          --+--------
          3 | 7 6 5 2
```

Applying *All From 9 and the Last From 10* to 7887 gives 2113.
Bring the first figure, 3, down into the answer.

We now multiply this by the flagged 2113 and put 6339 in the middle row. Then adding up the last four columns gives the remainder of 7652.

EXERCISE 3

Divide the following (do as many mentally as you can):

a 88)121 **b** 76)211 **c** 83)132 **d** 98)333

e 887)1223 **f** 867)1513 **g** 779)2222 **h** 765)3001

i 8907)13103 **j** 7999)12321 **k** 7789)21012 **l** 8888)44344

Next we consider the case where the answer consists of more than one digit.

EXAMPLE 6

1108 ÷ 79 = 13 remainder 81 = 14 remainder 2.

We set out the sum marking off two figures on the right (as we have a 2-figure divisor) and leave two rows as there are to be two answer figures.

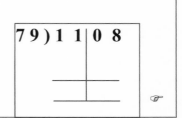

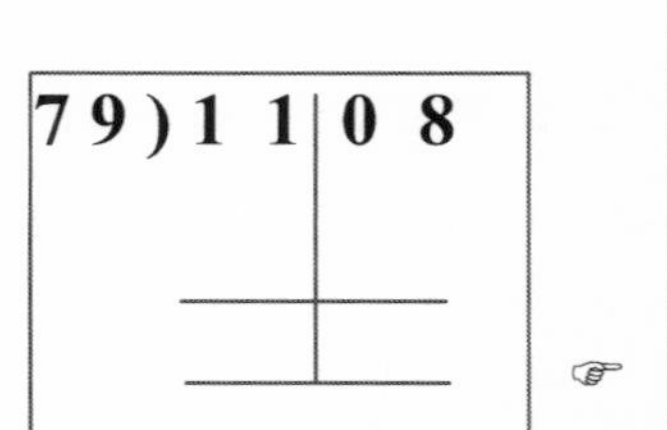

```
7 9 ) 1 1 | 0 8
```

☞

Bring the first 1 down into the answer. Multiply the flagged 21 by this 1 and put the answer (21) as shown in the second row.

```
79)1 1|0 8
21   2|1
      |6 3
------------
 1 3|8 1  = 14 remainder 2
```

Adding in the second column we get 3 which we put down and then multiply the 21 by this 3 to get 63, which we place as shown in the third row.

Add up the last two columns, but since the remainder, 81, is greater than the divisor, 79, there is another 79 contained in 81 so there are 14 79's in 1108 with 2 remaining.

EXAMPLE 7

1121123 ÷ 8989.

```
8989)1 1 2|1 1 2 3
1011   1 0|1 1
         2|0 2 2
          |4 0 4 4
-------------------
     1 2 4|6 4 8 7
```

The initial 1 comes down into the answer and multiplies the flagged 1011. This is placed as shown in the second row.

Adding in the second column we put 2 down in the answer and then multiply the 1011 by it. Put 2022 in the third row.

Adding in the third column we get 4 which we put down and also multiply by 1011.
So we put 4044 in the fourth row and then add up the last four columns to get the remainder.

Once the vertical line has been drawn in you can see the number of lines of working needed: this is the number of figures to the left of this line (3 figures and therefore 3 lines of working in the example above).

EXERCISE 4

Divide the following:

a 89)1021 **b** 88) 1122 **c** 79)1001 **d** 88)2111

e 97) 1111 **f** 888) 10011 **g** 887)11243 **h** 899)21212

i 988)30125 **j** 8899)201020

DIVISOR ABOVE A BASE NUMBER

A very similar method, but under the formula *Transpose and Apply* allows us to divide numbers which are above a base number.

EXAMPLE 8

1489 ÷ 123 = 12 remainder 13

Here we see that 123 is close to the base of 100 so we mark 2 figures off on the right.
In fact the method is just as before except that we write the flagged numbers as bar numbers:

$$\begin{array}{rrr|rr}
123\,) & 1 & 4 & 8 & 9 \\
\bar{2}\,\bar{3} & & \bar{2} & \bar{3} & \\
 & & & \bar{4} & 6 \\
\hline
 & 1 & 2 & 1 & 3
\end{array}$$

Bring the initial 1 down into the answer.
Multiply this 1 by the flagged $\overline{23}$ and write $\bar{2}$, $\bar{3}$.
Add in the second column and put down 2.
Multiply this 2 by the $\overline{23}$ and put down $\bar{4}, \bar{6}$.
Then add up the last two columns.

EXERCISE 5

Divide the following:

a 123)1377 **b** 131)1481 **c** 121)256 **d** 132)1366

e 1212)13545 **f** 161)1781 **g** 1003)321987 **h** 111)79999

Two other variations, where negative numbers come into the answer or remainder are worth noting.

EXAMPLE 9

Find 10121 ÷ 113.

$113)$	1	0	1	2	1
$\bar{1}\ \bar{3}$		$\bar{1}$	$\bar{3}$		
			1	3	
				1	3
	1	$\mathbf{\bar{1}}$	$\mathbf{\bar{1}}$	**6**	**4**

When we come to the second column we find we have to bring $\bar{1}$ down into the answer, multiplying this by the flagged $\bar{1}\,\bar{3}$ means we add 13 in the third row (two minuses make a plus).

The answer $1\bar{1}\bar{1}$ we finally arrive at is the same as 100 – 11 which is 89.

EXAMPLE 10

Find 2211 ÷ 112.

$112)$	2	2	1	1
$\bar{1}\ \bar{2}$		$\bar{2}$	$\bar{4}$	
			0	0
	2	**0**	$\mathbf{\bar{3}}$	**1**

$= 20$ rem $\overline{29}$ or 19 rem 83

20 remainder –29 means that 2211 is 29 short of 20 112's.
This means there are only 19 112's in 2211, so **we add 112 to –29** to get 19 remainder 83.

EXERCISE 6

Divide the following:

a 112)1234 **b** 121)3993 **c** 103)432 **d** 1012)21312

e 122)3333 **f** 123)2584 **g** 113)13696 **h** 1212)137987

i 111)79999 **j** 121)2652 **k** 1231)33033

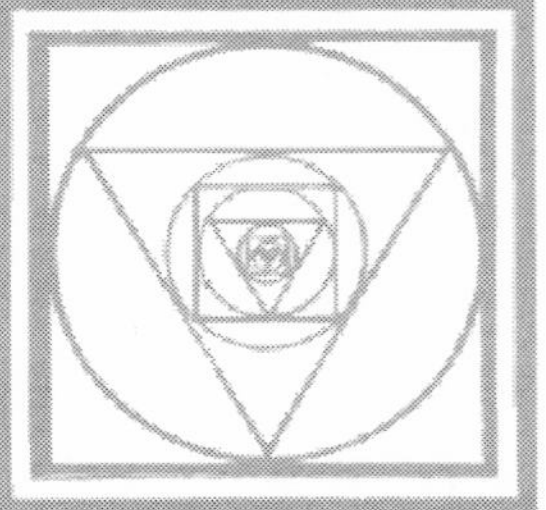

"George Parker Bidder (1806–1878) was asked, when he was ten, for the compound interest on £4,444 for 4,444 days at 4.5% per annum. He gave the answer £2,434 16s 5.25d in two minutes."

24

PERCENTAGE CHANGES

In this chapter we will be using some of our earlier special types of multiplication to find out what a certain quantity becomes when it is increased, or reduced, by a certain percentage.

 **EXAMPLE 1**

Increase 30 by 50%.

This means increase 30 by a half of 30.
And since half of 30 is 15 we increase 30 by 15 to get <u>45</u>.

 **EXAMPLE 2**

Reduce 16 by 25%.

This means take 25% of 16 away from 16.
Since 25% is a quarter and a quarter of 16 is 4, we take 4 from 16 to get <u>12</u>.

EXERCISE 1

Increase:	**a** 20 by 50%	**b** 44 by 50%	**c** 1000 by 50%	**d** 40 by 25%
	e 8 by 25%	**f** 30 by 10%	**g** 40 by 20%	**h** 24 by 100%
Reduce:	**i** 30 by 50%	**j** 200 by 50%	**k** 12 by 25%	**l** 80 by 25%
	m 32 by 25%	**n** 80 by 10%	**o** 500 by 1%	**p** 600 by 2%

INCREASING BY 10%

You will recall that there is a quick way of multiplying a number by 11.

EXAMPLE 3

Find **a** 34×11 **b** 77×11 **c** 357×11.

a $34 \times 11 = \underline{374}$ We simply put 7, the total of 3 and 4, between the 3 and the 4.

b $77 \times 11 = \underline{847}$ Here the total is 14 and we carry 1 to the left.

c $357 \times 11 = 38_127 = \underline{3927}$
Here 8 (the total of 3 and 5) and 12 (the total of 5 and 7) is placed between the 3 and the 7. When the 1 is carried we get an answer of $\underline{3927}$.

EXAMPLE 4

Find 54×1.1.

Multiplying by 1.1 is the same as multiplying by 11 except that the decimal point is put one place to the left: $54 \times 11 = 594$, therefore $54 \times 1.1 = \underline{59.4}$.

EXAMPLE 5

Increase 32 by 10%.

We increase a number by 10% by multiplying it by 1.1.
We therefore simply find 32×1.1. So $32 \times 1.1 = \underline{35.2}$.

We increase a number by 10% by multiplying it by 1.1.

EXERCISE 2

Multiply by 11:

a 26 **b** 41 **c** 53 **d** 67 **e** 84 **f** 38

g 88 **h** 73 **i** 333 **j** 345 **k** 712 **l** 2314

m 339 **n** 709 **o** 852 **p** 888

Multiply by 1.1:

q 42 **r** 35 **s** 72 **t** 66 **u** 234

Increase by 10%:

v 24 **w** 17 **x** 74 **y** 232 **z** 258

PERCENTAGE INCREASES

In a similar way we increase by 1%, 2% etc. by multiplying by 1.01, 1.02 etc.
And we know an easy way to multiply by numbers like 101, 102 . . .
So let us first revise this type of multiplication.

EXAMPLE 6

Find **a** 32 × 101 **b** 32 × 102 **c** 76 × 102 **d** 222 × 103.

a 32 × 101 = <u>3232</u>.

b 32 × 102 = <u>3264</u>. We put twice 32 on the right.

c 76 × 102 = $76_{1}52$ = <u>7752</u>. Twice 76 is 152 so we carry the 1.

d 222 × 103 = $222_{6}66$ = <u>22866</u>. We can have only 2 figures on the right when multiplying by 103.

EXERCISE 3

Find:

a 67 × 101 **b** 98 × 101 **c** 44 × 102 **d** 36 × 102

e 49 × 102 **f** 57 × 102 **g** 88 × 102 **h** 36 × 103

i 14 × 106 **j** 333 × 103 **k** 321 × 104 **l** 26 × 104

We increase a number by 1%, 2%, 3% . . .
by multiplying it by 1.01, 1.02, 1.03 . . .

EXAMPLE 7

Increase 43 by 2%.

Increasing by 2% is the same as multiplying by 1.02.
And we multiply by 1.02 by multiplying by 102 and placing the decimal point 2 places to the left.
So 43 × 1.02 = <u>43.86</u>.

EXERCISE 4

Increase:

a 23 by 3% **b** 41 by 2% **c** 88 by 1% **d** 34 by 2%

e 14 by 4% **f** 8 by 1% **g** 19 by 3% **h** 34 by 3% **i** 64 by 3%

j 26 by 7% **k** 222 by 2% **l** 123 by 3% **m** 50 by 5% **n** 55 by 6%

PERCENTAGE REDUCTIONS

Next we consider how to multiply a number by numbers just **under** 1, instead of just over 1.
We want to be able to multiply easily by numbers like 0.99, 0.98, 0.97.
So first we look at multiplying by 99, 98, 97 etc.

EXAMPLE 8

Find 23 × 99.

Remember that $99 = 10\bar{1}$. So $23 \times 99 = 23 \times 10\bar{1} = 23\overline{23} = \underline{2277}$

You can see that the answer, 2277, is formed from the 23 by first reducing it by 1 to get 22 (using *By One Less than the One Before*), and then applying *All from 9 and the Last from 10* to the 23 to get 77.

EXAMPLE 9

Find 23 × 98.

$23 \times 98 = 23 \times 10\bar{2} = 23\overline{46} = \underline{2254}$. We double 23 and apply *All from 9 . .* to 46 because 98 is 2 below 100.

EXAMPLE 10

Find 23 × 94.

$23 \times 94 = 23 \times 10\bar{6} = 23_{\bar{1}}\overline{38} = \underline{2162}$. Here we have to carry $\bar{1}$ to the left.

EXERCISE 5

Find:

a 67 × 99 **b** 48 × 99 **c** 39 × 99 **d** 19 × 99 **e** 91 × 99

f 44 × 98 **g** 73 × 98 **h** 98 × 98 **i** 56 × 98 **j** 71 × 98

k 33 × 97 **l** 44 × 97 **m** 16 × 97 **n** 82 × 97 **o** 8 × 97

p 55 × 96 **q** 22 × 96 **r** 33 × 93 **s** 41 × 92 **t** 34 × 91

To reduce by 1%, 2%, 3% . . .
we multiply by 0.99, 0.98, 0.97 . . .

That is, we multiply by $10\bar{1}$, $1.0\bar{2}$, $10\bar{3}$ . . .

EXAMPLE 11

Reduce 56 by 1%.

We find 56 × 0.99 and since 56 × 99 = 5544
therefore 56 × 0.99 = <u>55.44</u>

EXAMPLE 12

Reduce 56 by 3%.

We find 56 × 0.97 and as 56 × 97 = $56_{\bar{1}}\overline{68}$ = 5432
therefore 56 × 97 = <u>54.32</u>

EXERCISE 6

Reduce:

a 33 by 1% **b** 77 by 1% **c** 83 by 1% **d** 43 by 2%

e 26 by 2% **f** 78 by 2% **g** 32 by 3% **h** 32 by 5%

i 58 by 3% **j** 47 by 4% **k** 7 by 3% **l** 21 by 7%

m 59 by 4% **n** 11 by 9% **o** 28 by 22%

"Vedic Mathematics is that one field of knowledge which fulfils the purpose of education by developing the total creative genius of the individual, giving him the ability to be always spontaneously right and automatically precise so that his action, supported by Natural Law, is always effortlessly fulfilling."

Maharishi Mahesh Yogi

FOUNDER OF TRANSCENDENTAL MEDITATION

25

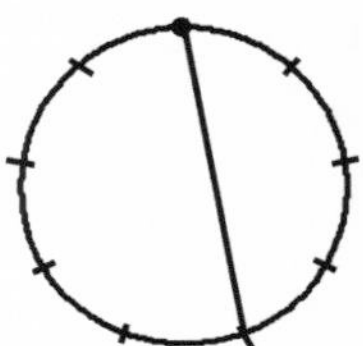

TRANSFORMATIONS

Something is transformed when it is changed in some way.
We will be considering four types of mathematical transformation:

Enlargement, **Reflection**, **Rotation**, and **Translation**.

ENLARGEMENT

If we take a square as an illustration we can see that there are different ways of enlarging it.

EXAMPLE 1

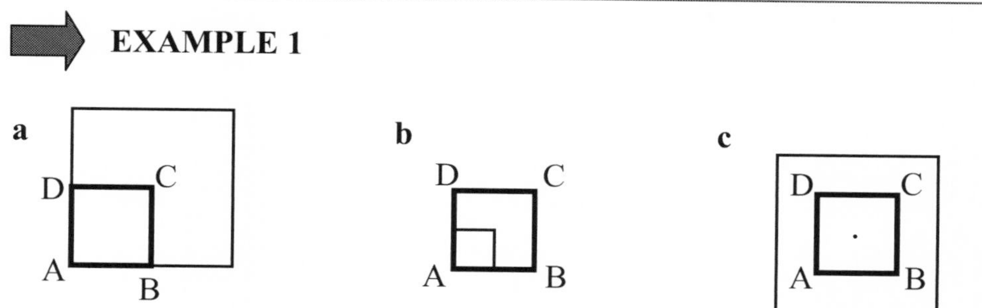

In both **a** and **c** above we start with a square ABCD and a larger square has been obtained from it. In both cases the larger square is double in size to the first square. We say that
the scale factor of the enlargement is 2.

The difference between **a** and **c** is that in **a** the enlargement is **from the point A**, whereas in **c** the enlargement is **from the centre of the first square**.
We say that **the centre of enlargement is at A** in **a** and at the centre of ABCD in **c**.

An enlargement is specified by **the centre of enlargement** and **the scale factor of the enlargement**.

Comparing **a** and **b** above note that the centre of enlargement is at A in both cases. The difference is that in **b** the original square has been reduced in size: its sides are in fact half those of the original square. The scale factor in this case is ½.

EXERCISE 1

In each diagram below the bold shape is being transformed. Copy the diagram, put a dot at the centre of enlargement and write down the scale factor of the enlargement:

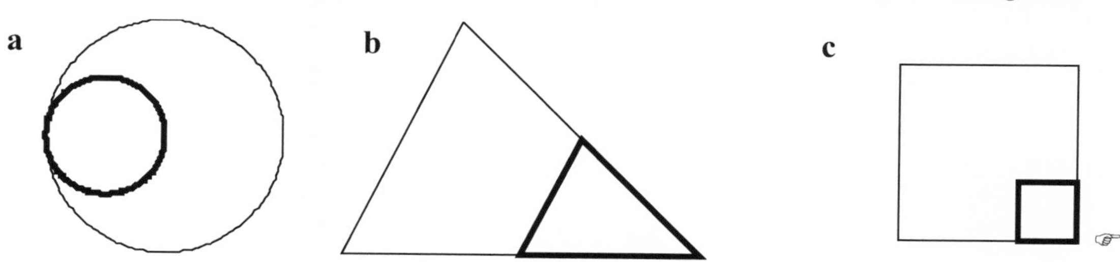

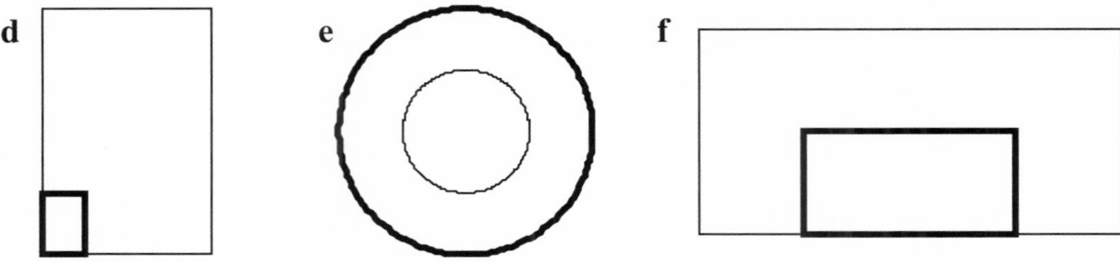

Note that in any kind of enlargement the **shape** of the original figure is not changed by the enlargement (a square is still a square when it is enlarged), only the **size** is altered.
Note also that if a figure is reduced in size we still call it an enlargement, but the scale factor will always then be a number less than 1.

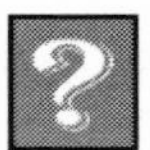

EXERCISE 2

Which shapes are enlargements of shape A (they may be turned):

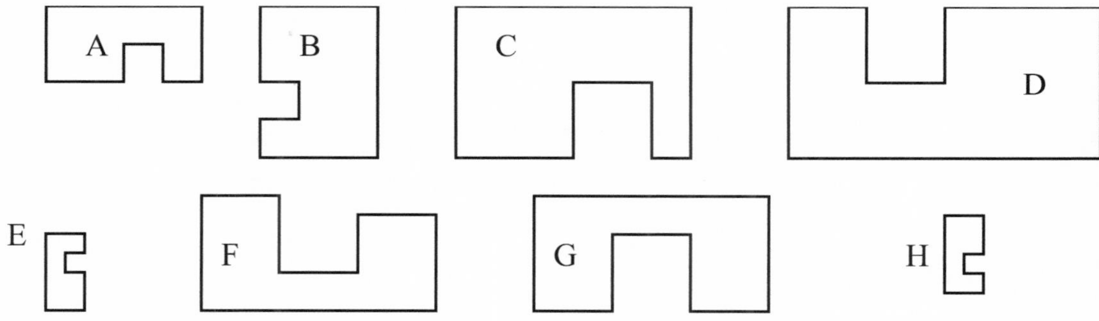

We may also be given a starting shape, a centre of enlargement and a scale factor and be asked to enlarge the starting shape.

EXAMPLE 2

Enlarge the trapezium ABCD by scale factor 2, using the mid-point of CD as centre of enlargement.

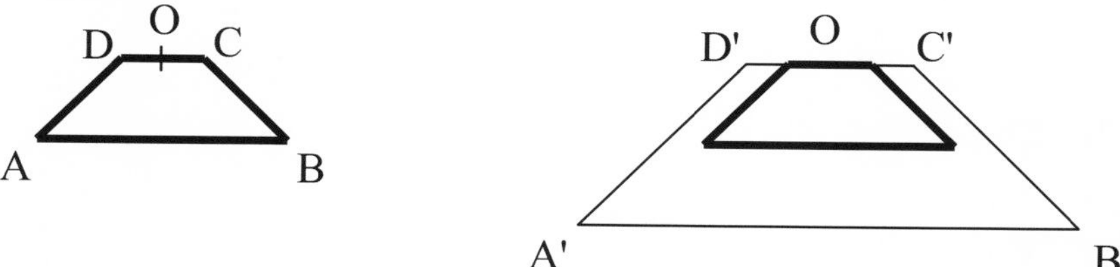

Since the scale factor of the enlargement is 2 each of the corners A,B,C and D must be twice as far from the centre of enlargement than in the original shape. So ABCD has been enlarged to A'B'C'D'.

❋ Measure the distances of A, B, C and D from the centre of enlargement, O, and check that these are doubled in the enlargement.

Enlargements come under the *Proportionately* Sutra of Vedic Mathematics.

EXAMPLE 3

Enlarge the triangle ABC shown using X as the centre of enlargement and a scale factor of 2.

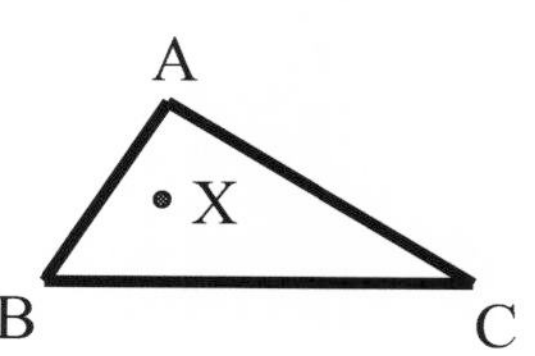

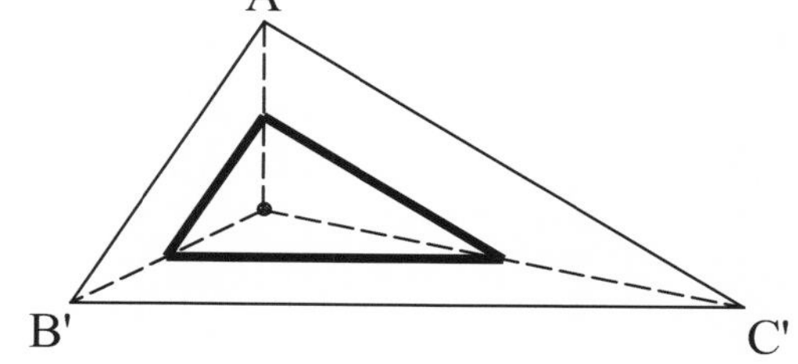

We draw a line from X to A and since the scale factor is 2 we extend this line until it is twice its original length. This gives us the point A' shown on the right above.

Similarly we extend the lines XB and XC to get B' and C' and then complete the triangle.

1 On a sheet of graph paper number 0 to 8 on the x-axis and 0 to 5 on the y-axis. Draw the triangle with vertices at (1,2), (5,2) and (2,4).
Using (2,3) as a centre of enlargement and a scale factor of 2 draw an enlargement of the triangle.

EXERCISE 3

For each of the enlargements below start with a rectangle ABCD which has base AB = 2cm and height BC = 1cm (use squared paper and label the enlargements A'B'C'D'):

	Centre of Enlargement	**Scale Factor**
a	A	3
b	D	2
c	centre of rectangle	2
d	mid-point of AB	3
e	mid-point of BC	2
f	C	½
g	1cm to the left of A	2

For each of the enlargements below start with an equilateral triangle ABC where BC is the base and BC = 2cm (use triangular spotty paper and label the enlarged triangles A'B'C');

	Centre of Enlargement	**Scale Factor**
h	A	3
i	centre of triangle	½
j	centre of triangle	2
k	B	1½
l	mid-point of BC	3
m	1cm above A	2

REFLECTION

Some shapes are symmetrical. For example the letter A has a symmetry: we could draw a vertical line through it and each half would be a reflection of the other half:

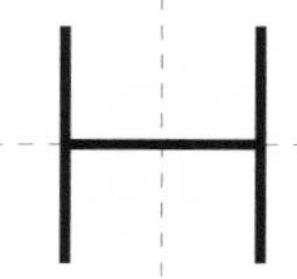

Similarly the letter H has two lines of symmetry, one vertical and one horizontal.

2 Write out the letters C D E M T W X Y Z and draw in the lines of symmetry.

We reflect a shape when we are given one half of the shape and the position of the line of symmetry. We use the *Transpose and Apply* formula.

EXAMPLE 4

Reflect the shape in the line XY.

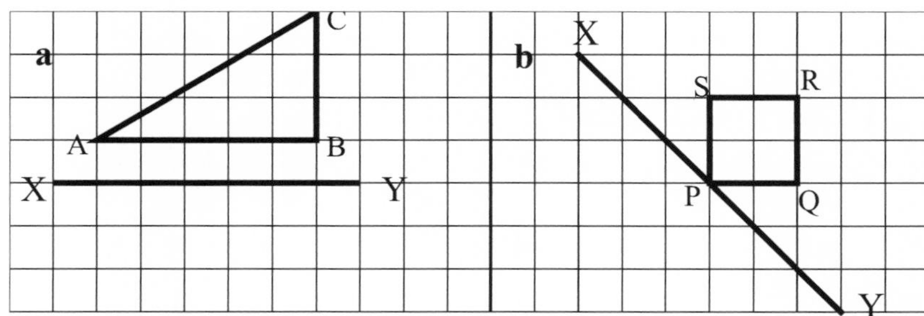

The reflection is always as far behind the mirror as the object is in front of it and so we can find the reflection of each of the corner points of the shape and join them up.

So the reflection of A is 1 unit below the line XY, and so is the reflection of B. C is 4 units above the line so we mark a point, C', 4 units below it. Then we can complete the triangle. ☞

In part **b** we must be more careful. P is on the line and so it will remain there. How far is Q from the line XY?

It is 1 square diagonal from the line, and so we measure a further diagonal on the other side of XY and mark a point Q'. Similarly for S.

R is 2 diagonals from XY so we extend 2 further diagonals on the other side of XY and then join up the square.

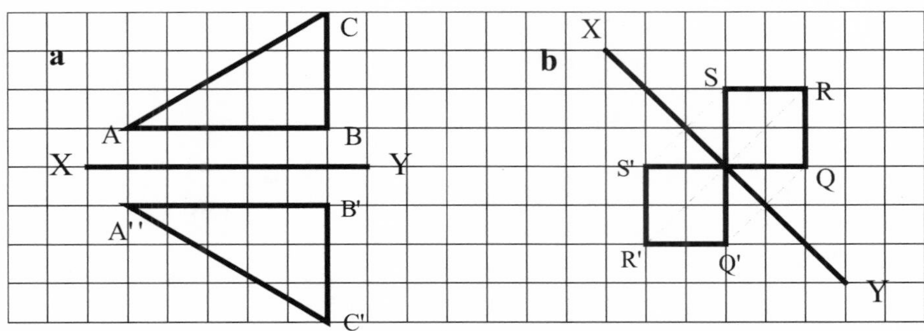

EXERCISE 4

Copy the following shapes onto square dotty paper and reflect them in the line XY:

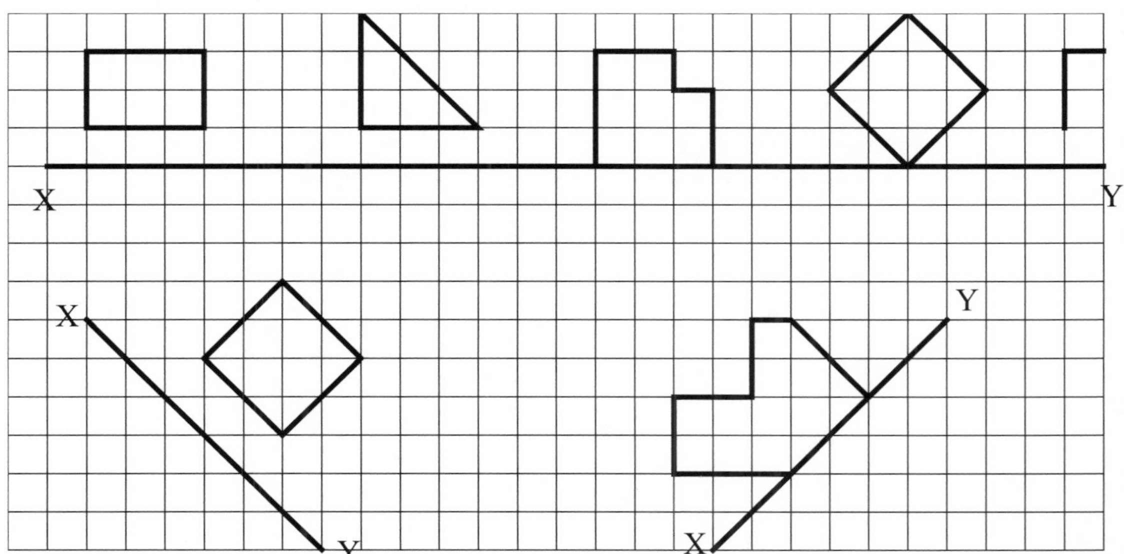

EXERCISE 5

Copy the following shapes and shade in the fewest number of extra squares that will make the shape symmetrical about XY:

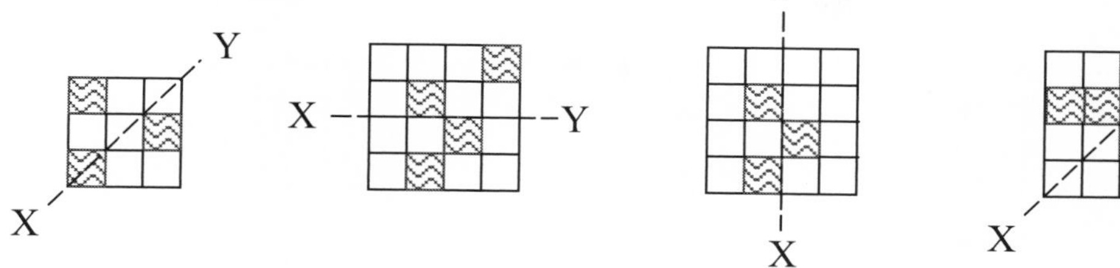

ROTATION

Another way in which objects can be transformed is by rotating them.

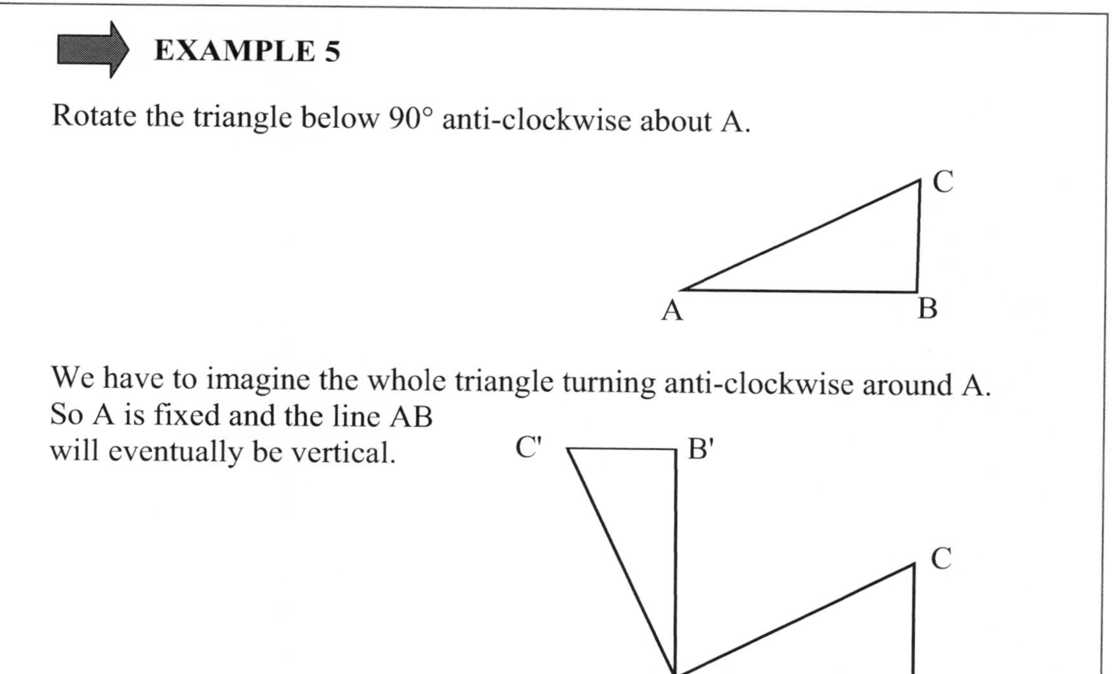

EXAMPLE 5

Rotate the triangle below 90° anti-clockwise about A.

We have to imagine the whole triangle turning anti-clockwise around A. So A is fixed and the line AB will eventually be vertical.

We see that three things need to be specified in order to carry out a rotation, in addition to the object itself which is being rotated:

To rotate an object we need to know:
1) the centre of the rotation
2) the direction of rotation (clockwise or anti-clockwise)
3) the angle of rotation.

The one exception to this is 180° rotations which do not need a direction because the result is the same whether you rotate clockwise or anti-clockwise.

EXAMPLE 6

Rotate the shape below 90° clockwise about the point marked O.

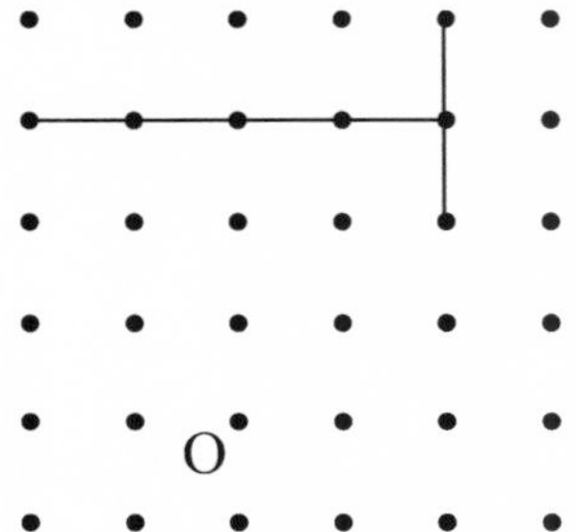

It may not be so obvious where the rotated shape will go here.
But we may note that the point in the middle of the horizontal line is 3 units vertically up from O, and so it will rotate to the point 3 units to the right of O.
It is then not difficult to draw in the rest of the figure.

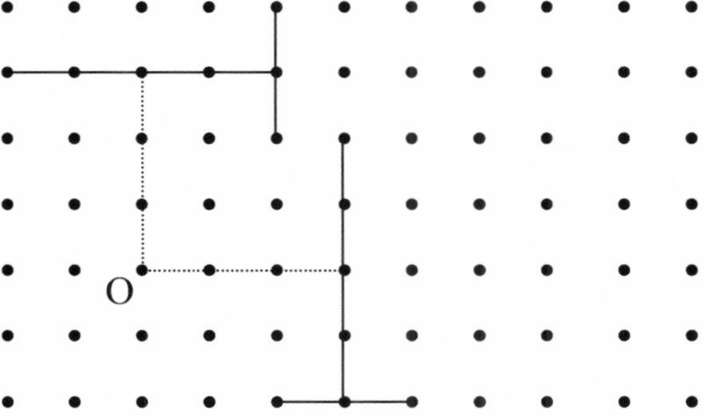

Note that with rotations the shape and the size of the object being rotated are not affected by the rotation, only the position is affected.

Rotations come under the Sutras *By Alternate Elimination and Retention* and *By Mere Observation* because we usually mentally rotate a part of a figure (a point or line) first, ignoring the rest of the shape, and then add the rest of it.

For more difficult rotations or as a check tracing paper can be used. Place the tracing paper over the shape to be rotated and trace it. Then put your pen or pencil on the centre of rotation and keep it there while you turn the paper by the angle given. You will then see where the rotated shape goes.

EXERCISE 6

Use square spotty paper and carry out the rotations below.
The object for each of these is a triangle like the one in Example 5 but with a base of 4cm and a height of 1cm. Label your rotated shape A'B'C'.

	Centre of Rotation	**Direction of Rotation**	**Angle of Rotation**
a	A	clockwise	90°
b	B	clockwise	90°
c	B	anti-clockwise	90°
d	C	-	180°
e	mid-point of AB	anti-clockwise	90°
f	1cm below A	clockwise	90°
g	2cm above mid-point of AB	clockwise	90°
h	1cm above and 1cm to the right of C	-	180°

EXERCISE 7

Use triangular spotty paper for the following:

a Draw an equilateral triangle ABC, where the base AB is 2cm.
Rotate this 60° clockwise about A.
Now rotate both triangles, as a single figure, 120° clockwise about C.

b Draw a regular hexagon ABCDEF of side 2cm, where AB is the base and the vertices are labelled in an anti-clockwise direction.
Rotate the figure 180° about D.
Also rotate both shapes, as a single figure, 120° clockwise about A.

c Draw a rhombus ABCD of side 1cm, where AB is the base and vertices labelled in an anti-clockwise direction again.
Rotate ABCD 120° clockwise about C and also 120° anti-clockwise about C.
Rotate the whole shape thus formed **i** 120° clockwise about A.
ii 120° anti-clockwise about A.

TRANSLATION

A translation occurs when a shape is moved from one position to another without turning it or changing it in any other way.

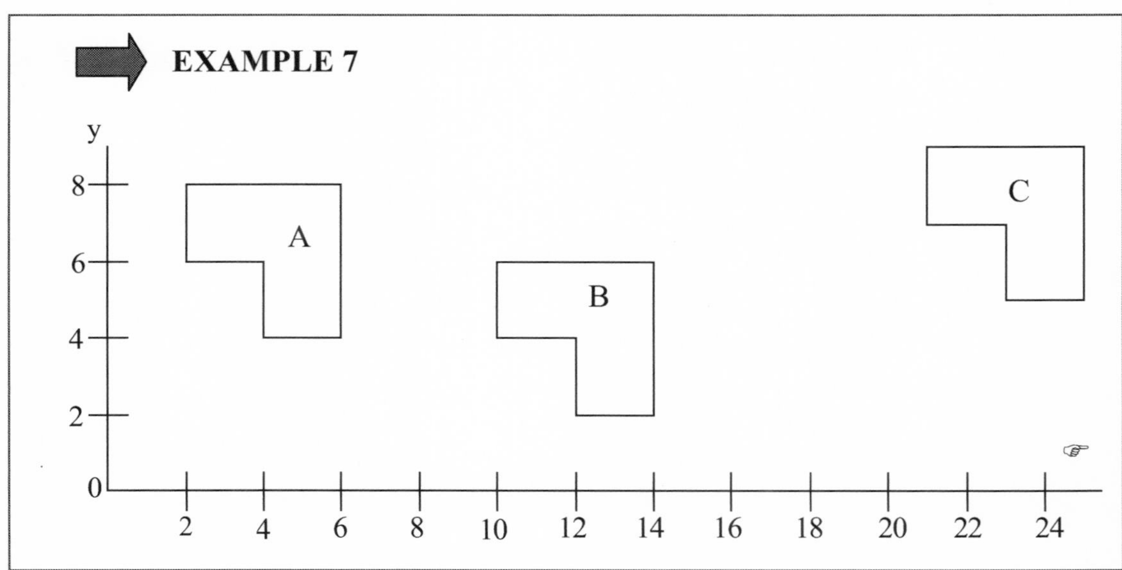

In this graph shape A has been translated to B.

To describe a translation precisely we only need to specify how much the original shape has
been moved horizontally, and how much it has been moved vertically.

Since shape A has moved 8 units to the right and 2 units down we say that the translation is $\begin{bmatrix} 8 \\ -2 \end{bmatrix}$ where the 8 is the horizontal movement and –2 indicates 2 units downwards.

Similarly to translate shape C to B the translation would be $\begin{bmatrix} -11 \\ -3 \end{bmatrix}$ because we have to move C 11 units to the left and 3 units down.

The top number in a translation is the horizontal part of the translation
and
the bottom number is the vertical part.
Translations are positive to the right and positive upwards,

They come under the *By Addition and By Subtraction* formula.

3 What translation moves C to A?

4 What translation moves B to A?

5 What translation moves A to C?

EXERCISE 8

a The square A with coordinates (2,2), (4,2), (4,4), (2,4) is translated by $\begin{bmatrix} -4 \\ -3 \end{bmatrix}$.

What will be the coordinates of the square after the translation?
What translation will move the square back to A? ☞

b

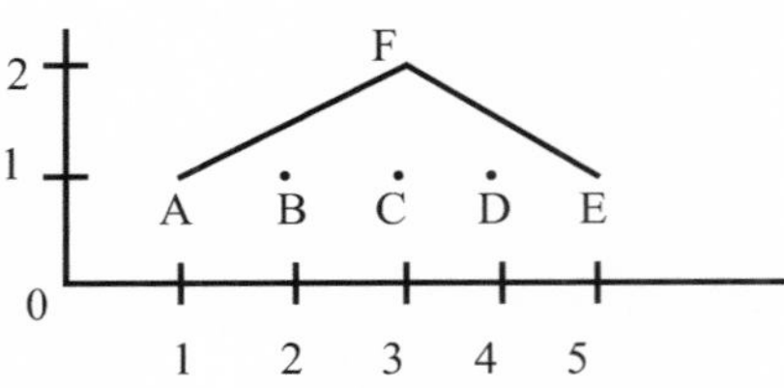

This figure consists of 3 dots and 2 lines.

What will be the coordinates of A, B, C, D, E and F after the translation $\begin{bmatrix} 2 \\ 3 \end{bmatrix}$?

c A pentagon, A, has coordinates (0,0), (–2,–2), (–4,–2), (–6,0), (–3,2).

Draw the pentagon, A, and translate it, by $\begin{bmatrix} 10 \\ 4 \end{bmatrix}$ to B.

Then translate the pentagon, A, by $\begin{bmatrix} 4 \\ 0 \end{bmatrix}$ to get shape C.

What translation will move B to C?

We can also combine the various transformations together, as shown in the next exercise.

EXERCISE 9

You will need graph or squared paper:

a Number your x-axis from 0 to 9 and your y-axis from 0 to 7.
Draw the rectangle A(1,2), B(4,2), C(4,4), D(1,4). Label this P.
Reflect P in the line y=2. Label this Q.
Rotate P 90° clockwise about C. Label this R.

Translate P by $\begin{bmatrix} 5 \\ -2 \end{bmatrix}$. Label this S.

Enlarge P with C as centre of enlargement and scale factor ½. Label this T.

b Using ½cm for 1 unit on each axis, number the x-axis from –6 to 28
and the y-axis from 0 to 16.
Plot the rectangle (0,0), (2,0), (2,1), (0,1).

☞

i Rotate the rectangle 90° clockwise about the bottom right corner of the rectangle,

ii Enlarge the rotated rectangle, scale factor 2, with centre at the bottom right of the rectangle.

Now go back to instruction **i** and repeat instructions **i** and **ii** as many times as you can.

c Label axes from 0 to 9 on the x-axis and 0 to 7 on the y-axis.
Plot the right-angled triangle (1,1), (3,1), (3,2).
Rotate the triangle 90° clockwise about (3,1). Label this P.
Reflect P in the line y=3. Label this Q.
Rotate Q 90° clockwise about (5,3). Label this R.
Reflect R in the line x=6. Label this S.
Describe the rotation that transforms S back onto the original triangle.

"The mathematician does not study pure mathematics because it is useful; he studies it because he delights in it and he delights in it because it is beautiful."

Henri Poincaré (1854–1912)

FRENCH MATHEMATICIAN

26

CONSTRUCTIONS

In ancient Greek times geometrical constructions could only be properly carried out using two geometrical instruments: a straight edge and compasses.

This was because the straight line and the circle were considered to be fundamental forms from which all other forms could be created.

Today we have other instruments like protractors, set squares etc. but in this chapter we will use only ruler and compasses. Plain paper should be used for the work in this chapter.

BISECTING A LINE

Suppose we have a straight line, drawn with our ruler, and that we want to cut the line in half (bisect it).

❋ Draw a horizontal line about 6cm long (the length is not important) with some space above and on each side of it.

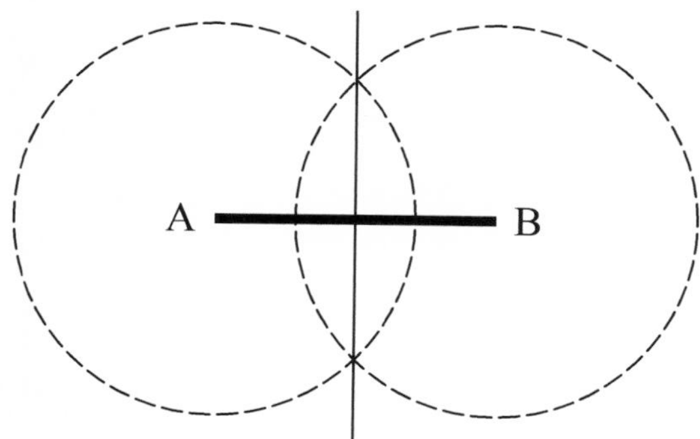

Suppose the line is AB in the diagram.
Put your compass point on A and open your compasses until the pencil is over half of the distance from A to B.
Draw a circle, as shown.
Without altering the compass setting put the point on B and draw another circle.
Join the points of intersection of the two circles.
This line bisects the original line.

It is usual for all construction lines to be drawn faintly on the paper with only the required result being drawn in boldly at the end.

EXERCISE 1

a Draw an oblique (slanting) line and find the centre of it using this method. Note that it is not essential to draw full circles, you could just draw arcs where you expect the intersections to be, as shown below.

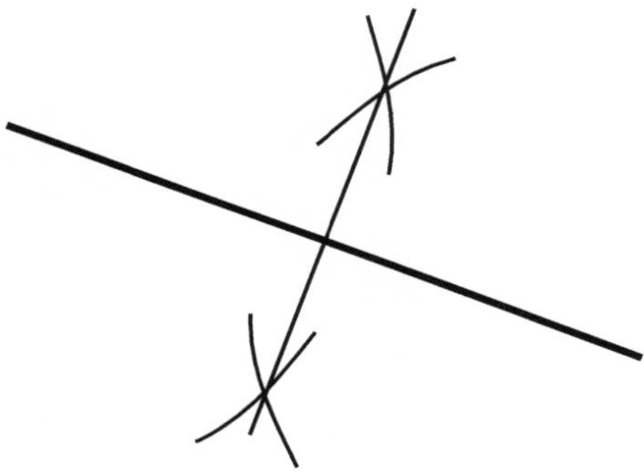

☞

b Construct a triangle with sides 3, 6 and 7cm.
Bisect each of the three sides of the triangle. If you are accurate you should find that the three lines meet at a single point. This point is called the **circumcentre**.

c The circumcentre is the centre of a circle which goes through all three vertices of the triangle. Put your compass point on the circumcentre and draw a circle which passes through the three vertices of the triangle. This is called the **circumcircle**.

This simple bisection construction gives us more than just the mid-point of the line, it also gives us four right angles where the two lines intersect. The constructed line is therefore called the **perpendicular bisector**.

1 Draw a line about 6cm long. Suppose that we want to construct a right angle at each end of the line.

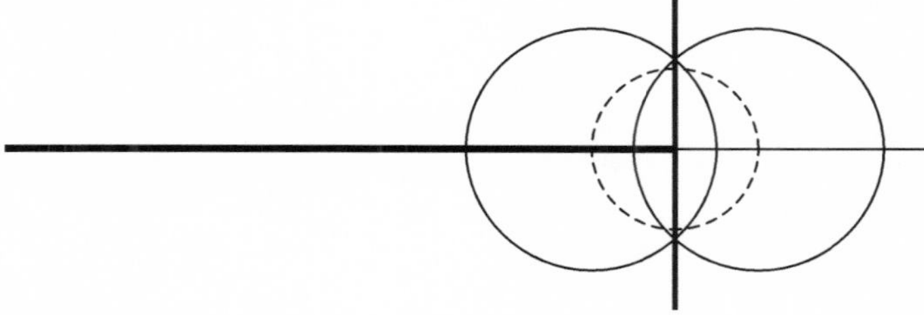

Starting at the right end of the line (shown in bold above) first extend the line to the right and draw a circle (shown dashed) centred on the end of the line.

Use the two points where this circle cuts the horizontal line as centres to draw two more, larger, circles which intersect. The vertical line can then be drawn in.
Finish the construction at the right end of your line and then make a right-angle at the left-hand end of your line by the same method.

EXERCISE 2

a Construct a triangle with sides 4, 5 and 6cm.
Bisect the three sides and hence draw in the circumcircle.

b Draw an oblique line 8cm long.
Construct a right-angle at each end of the line and complete a rectangle of height 5cm.

BISECTING AN ANGLE

Suppose we have the angle ABC and that we want to draw a line which bisects the angle.

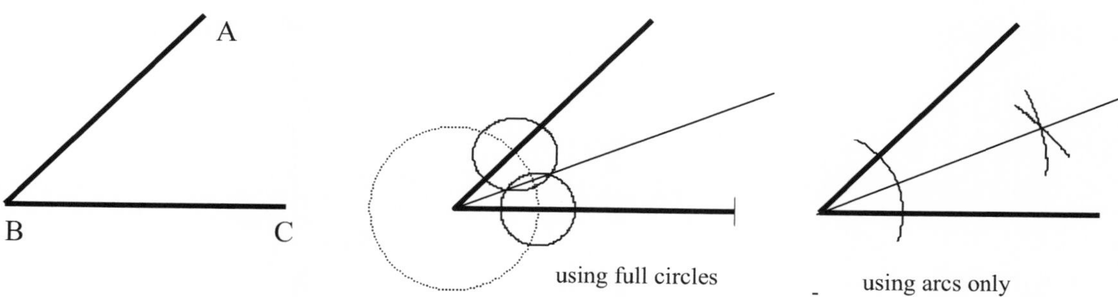

We first draw a circle centred on the corner B (shown dotted).
This circle cuts the two arms of the angle in two points. We use these points as centres for two more circles which must be the same size as each other and which must intersect.
The bisector can then be drawn from the corner B, through these intersection points and on.

EXERCISE 3

In this exercise, except for part **a**, you may use full circles in the constructions or only arcs.

a Draw two angles like the one above and bisect them using the two methods shown above.

b Now draw an obtuse angle and bisect it in the same way.

c Construct a triangle with sides 3, 6 and 7cm.
Bisect all three of the angles of your triangle.

The three angle bisectors of a triangle always meet in a single point.
Check that your bisectors meet in one point, or very nearly.
This point is called the **incentre** of the triangle.

☞

From the incentre it is possible to draw a circle that touches all three sides of the triangle.

d Put your compass point on your incentre and draw the **incircle**, just touching all the sides without going outside the triangle.

A line which just touches a circle without going inside it is called a **tangent**.

CONSTRUCTING ANGLES

Bisecting angles allows us to construct various angles without using a protractor.

EXERCISE 4

a Construct a right angle by the method shown earlier.
Bisect the right-angle. What angle have you formed? (How many degrees?)

b Draw a base line AB of length 5cm.
Draw a circle of radius 5cm centred on A and another centred on B.
Complete the equilateral triangle.
Bisect the angle at A. What angle have you formed?

c Bisect the angle at B in your equilateral triangle. Call the two halves p (below) and q (above).
Bisect angle p. What angle have you formed?

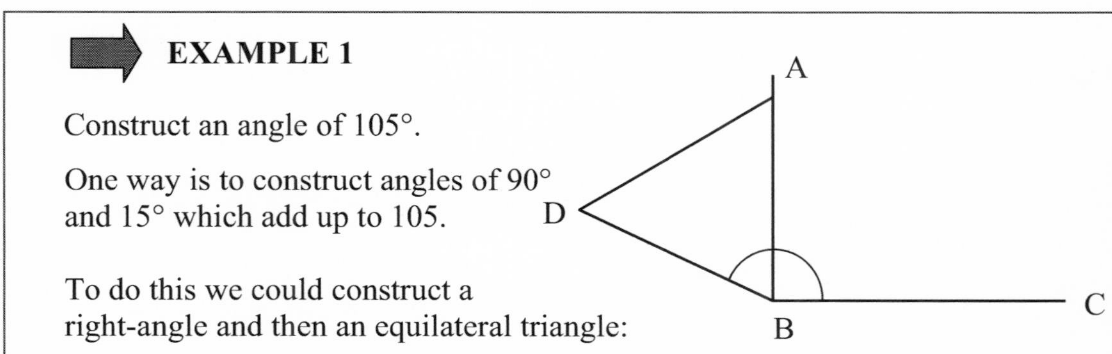

EXAMPLE 1

Construct an angle of 105°.

One way is to construct angles of 90° and 15° which add up to 105.

To do this we could construct a right-angle and then an equilateral triangle:

2 Construct the right-angle ABC using only ruler and compasses.
Construct an equilateral triangle on one arm of the right-angle as shown above.
Now bisect angle B of the triangle and bisect the upper part again so that the 15° angle you
get is next to the line AB. Mark clearly your 105° angle.

3 In the above diagram what size is the angle DBC?

EXERCISE 5

a Construct a triangle with sides 4, 5 and 6cm.
Bisect all three angles to find the incentre and draw the incircle.

b Construct an angle of 120° by adding two 60° angles.

c Construct an angle of 120° by adding 30° to 90°.

d Construct an angle of 135°.

e An angle of 105° can also be constructed by adding angles of 45° and 60°.
Construct the 105° angle in this way.

THE GOLDEN RECTANGLE

There is a certain shape of rectangle which has many remarkable properties.
The ratio of its sides is called the **golden ratio** because the ratio arises in all sorts of ways and in many different areas of study.

The golden rectangle can be constructed as follows.

EXERCISE 6

a Using ruler and compasses construct a square ABCD of side about 8cm. Be sure to have at least 5cm of space to the right of it. Extend AB about 5cm. ☞

b Bisect the base to find the mid-point, M, and join M to the top right vertex of the square.

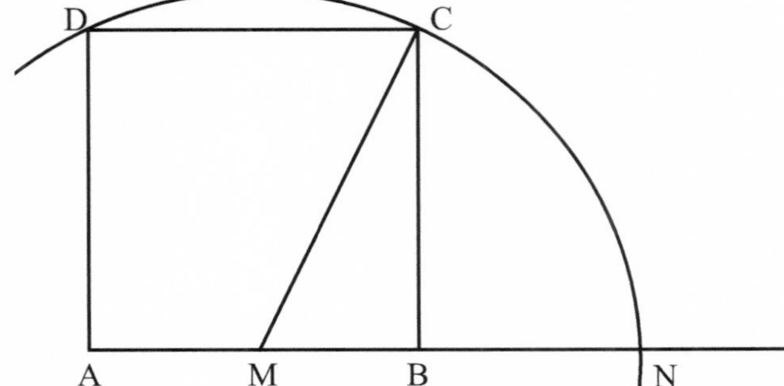

c Draw a circle (or part of a circle) with M as centre and MC as radius. This gives you the point N on the base line.

d N, A and D are three corners of the golden rectangle. So construct a perpendicular at N and extend the line DC to meet this perpendicular.

e Draw over your golden rectangle to make it stand out.

This rectangle is said to have the most pleasing shape and artists and architects have used the it in their designs.

Next you can produce another golden rectangle by copying the one you have just made, as explained in the next exercise.

EXERCISE 7

a First draw a base line faintly about 15cm long with some space above it.

b Measure the side AN by putting your compass point on A and opening it until the pencil is on N exactly. Put the point on one end of your base line and mark off the distance on the other end. Draw in the base of your golden rectangle.

c Now measure the height of your rectangle in the same way. Put your compass point on each end of your new construction and make an arc above it where you expect the top corners to be.

d Measure a diagonal of your golden rectangle and transfer it to the new construction. That means put the point at one base corner and make an arc where you expect the opposite corner to be. This should cut the previous mark. Transfer both diagonals in this way and then complete the golden rectangle.

Next we will use this diagram to illustrate another beautiful property of the golden rectangle.

e We want to form a square on the left side of the rectangle. Measure the height of your rectangle with your compasses and mark off this distance from both left corners to get the points X and Y. Join XY to form a square.

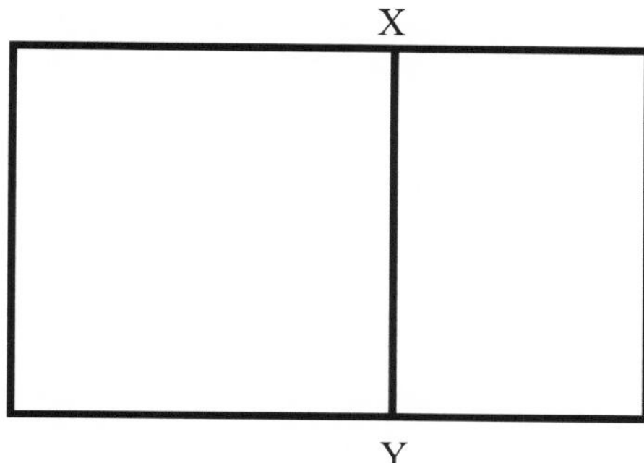

It is a remarkable fact that the smaller rectangle produced in this way is also a golden rectangle.

f Now we repeat this process by constructing a square in the top part of the smaller golden rectangle. Measure the top of the rectangle with compasses and mark off the distance on the long sides.

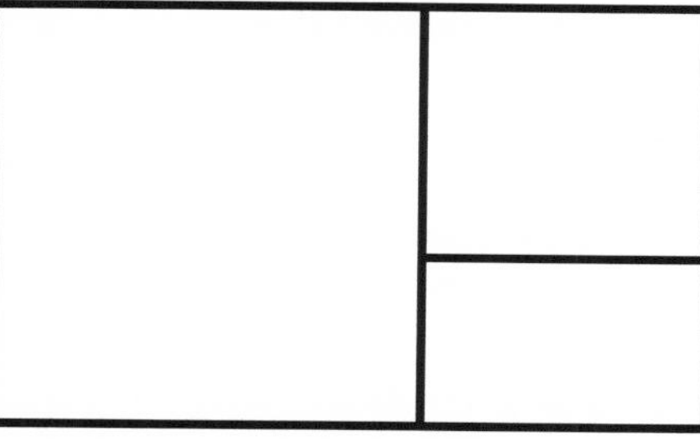

☞

g The small rectangle produced is again a golden rectangle. Repeat this again by forming a square on the right of the smallest rectangle, and then again by forming a square on the bottom of the smallest rectangle.

h If you can see how the squares you have been drawing spiral round in a clockwise direction you may be able to draw in some more golden rectangles. Do as many as you can.

i It is now possible to draw in the **golden spiral**:

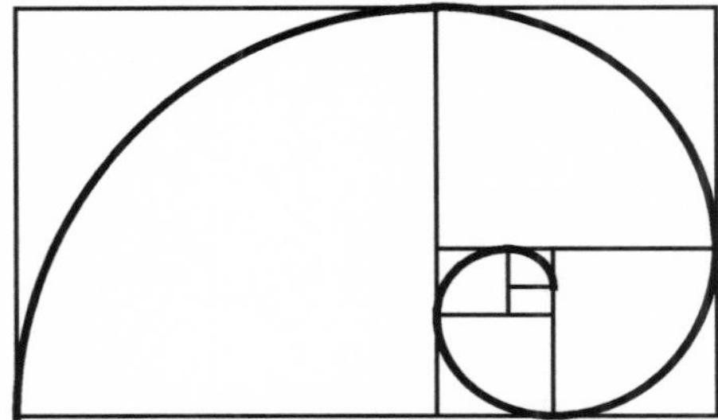

The spiral goes on spiralling in towards a central point.
It is also possible to extend the spiral outwards by adding a square on the bottom and then on the right and so on indefinitely.

THE PENTAGRAM

First we construct a pentagon as follows:

EXERCISE 8

a Draw a base line AB about 6cm long in the middle of your page.

b From each end of the line draw a circle with radius equal to the length of the base line.

c At the lower point of intersection of these circles draw another circle the same size as the first two. The two lower points where this circle meets the other two circles we call X and Y.

d Bisect the line AB. Where this bisector meets the top of the lower circle we call Z.

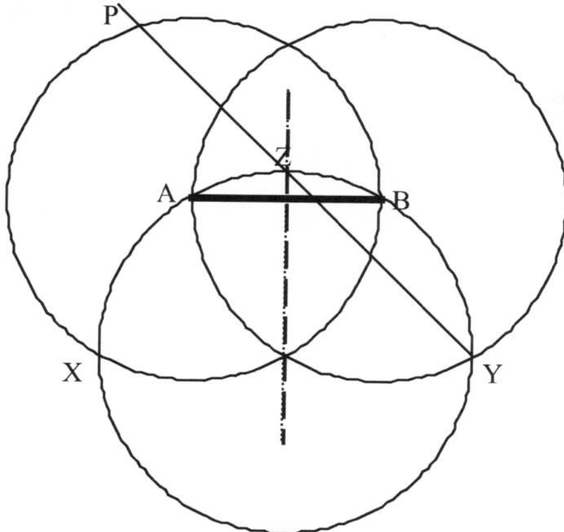

e Next draw a line from Y to Z and extend it until it meets the top left circle at P. Similarly extend the line XZ until it meets the top right circle at Q.

f Join AP and BQ. These are two more sides of the pentagon.

g To find the top corner of the pentagon take your compasses, still set at the radius of the circles and with the point on P make an arc where you expect the top corner of the pentagon to be. Make a similar mark from Q. Where they intersect is the top corner so you can now complete the pentagon.

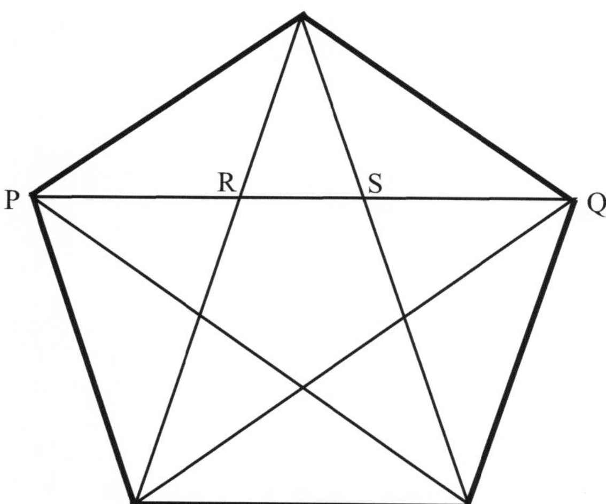

h Finally you can **draw in the pentagram** by **joining all five diagonals** of the pentagon in bold or with a colour. ☞

Note that each diagonal cuts each other diagonal at two points. So PQ for example is cut at R and at S.

The pentagram is full of golden ratios: PR:RS is a golden ratio,
and so is QS:SR
and PQ:PS and PQ:RQ.

Similarly for all the other diagonals.

Give me a place on which to stand and I can move the earth
Archimedes (287–212 BC)
GREEK MATHEMATICIAN

And when Hieron was sruck with amazement and asked him [Archimedes] to reduce the problem to practice and to give an illustration of some great weight moved by a small force, he fixed upon a ship of burden with three masts from the king's arsenal which had only been drawn up with great labour and many men; and loading her with many passengers and a full freight, sitting himself the while far off, with no great endeavour but only holding the end of a compound pulley quietly in his hand and pulling at it, he drew the ship along smoothly and safely as if it were moving through the sea.
Proclus (410–85 AD)
GREEK PHILOSOPHER

27

PARALLEL LINES & BEARINGS

PARALLEL LINES

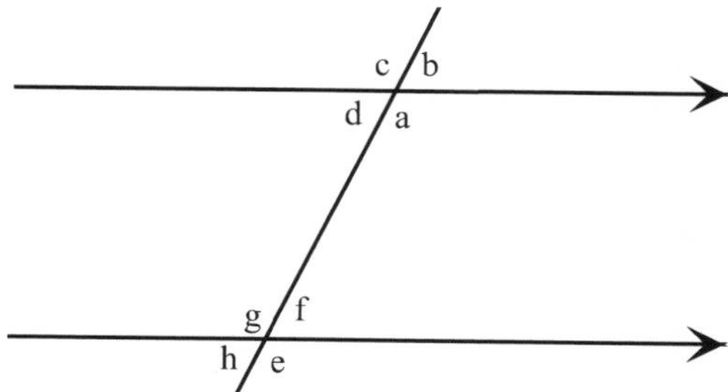

The arrows on the two lines above means that they are exactly parallel.

The line cutting across the parallel lines produces the eight angles a, b . . . h.

❋ Some of these angles are equal: which do you think are equal?

Angles b and d will be equal because b and c add up to 180° and so do d and c. Angles which are equal in this way are called **vertically opposite angles**.

Similarly a = c, e = g and h = f.
This means that a, c, e and g are all equal and that b, d, f and h are all equal.

Angles like a and e which form an **F** shape are equal (we can imagine the angle sliding down the oblique line until it fits exactly at e): we will call these F-angles.

Angles like d and f, which form a **Z** shape are therefore also equal: we will be referring to these as Z-angles.

c and g are also F-angles and a and g are also Z-angles.

EXAMPLE 1

Find angles a, b and c.

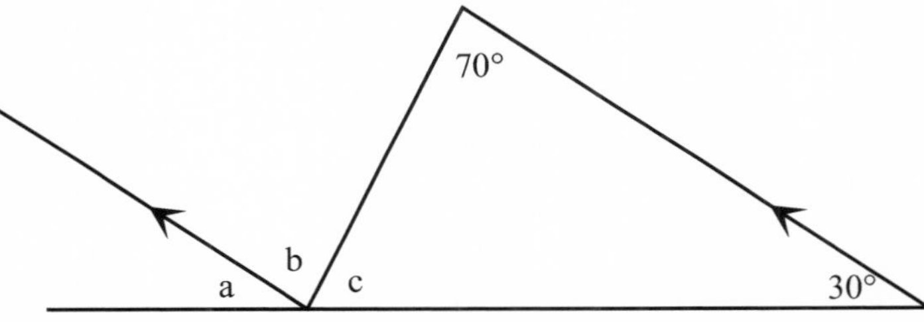

Here we see a pair of parallel lines and so we can look for vertically opposite angles and F and Z-angles.

There are no vertically opposite angles in the diagram, but there is a pair of F-angles and a pair of Z-angles.

b = 70° because b and the 70° angle are Z-angles,
and a = 30° because a and the 30° angle are F-angles.

Since a+b+c = 180° we can then get c, so c = 80°.

EXAMPLE 2

Find angles a,b and c.

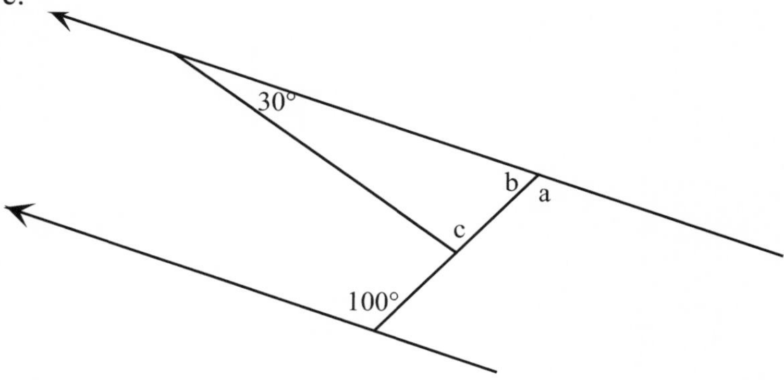

Here we may notice a pair of Z-angles.

a = 100° because a and the 100° angle are Z-angles, and since a+b = 180°, b = 80°.
Since the angles in a triangle total 180° we then get c = 70°.

EXAMPLE 3

Find w, x, y, z.

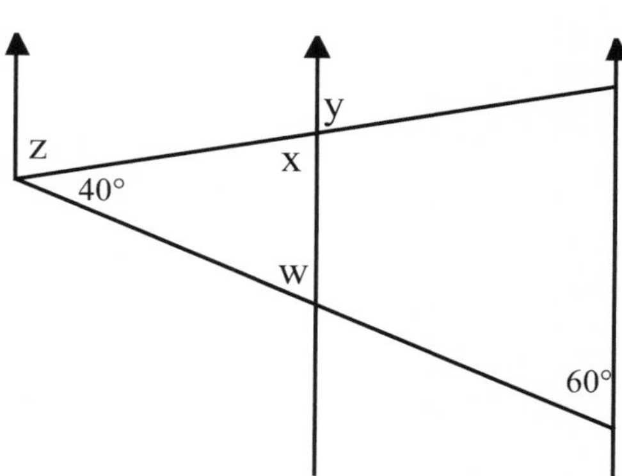

Here we have 3 parallel lines.
There are 2 pairs of F-angles, a pair of Z-angles and a pair of vertically opposite angles.

w = 60° (they are F-angles),
therefore x = 80° (three angles in a triangle),
x=y (vertically opposite) so y = 80°,
and z=x (they are Z-angles) so z = 80°.

This is not the only way of solving this problem.

We can summarise these results about angles in parallel lines as follows:

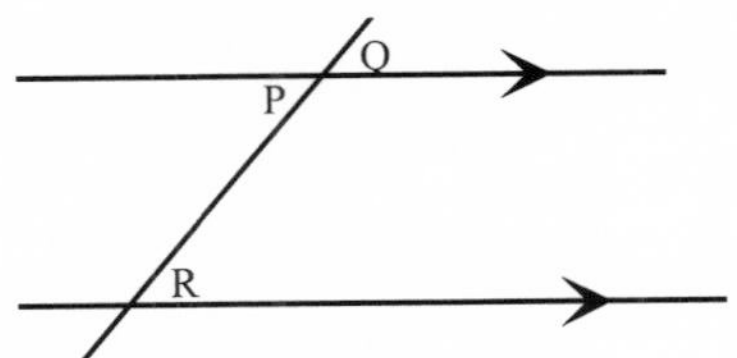

P= Q as these are vertically opposite,
Q= R as these are F-angles,
P= R as these are Z-angles.

EXERCISE 1

Find the angles marked with letters:

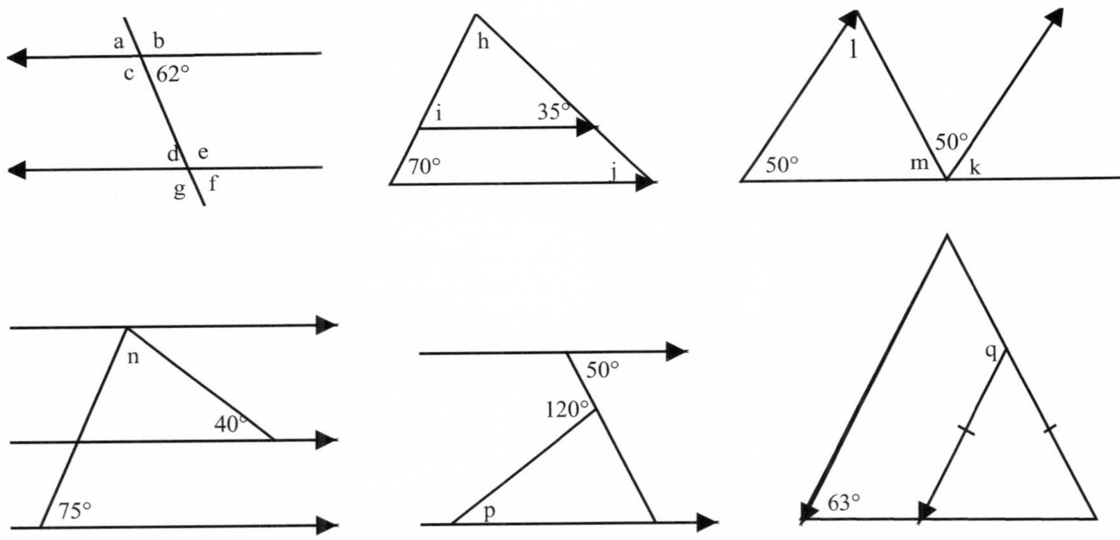

SCALE DRAWING

Plans and maps are very useful where large structures are to be studied or built. These are examples of scale drawings where the shape of every detail is the same as in the original but the size is much smaller. This is very similar to enlargements dealt with in the chapter before the last, where the scale factor is less than 1.

EXAMPLE 4

A rectangular lawn measures 45m by 30m. By drawing a plan of the lawn find the distance between opposite corners of the lawn.

We need to select a suitable scale: if we use 1m = 1cm the rectangle will still be rather large. So we may choose 5m = 1cm which will make the rectangle 9cm by 6cm.

- Draw this rectangle on squared paper. Write the scale: 5m=1cm next to it.
- Measure the length of a diagonal: you should get about 10.8cm (anything between 10.7 and 10.9 is acceptable).

Since 1cm is equivalent to 5m we must multiply the 11cm by 5 to get an answer of about 55m.

The scale of 5m = 1cm can also be written as 500:1 because 5m=500cm and so the lawn size has been reduced by a scale factor of 500.

EXAMPLE 5

A triangular plot of land measures 200m by 144m by 120m. Find the distance from the mid-point of the longest side to the opposite corner.

Again we must first decide on a suitable scale.
If we choose 20m = 1cm then we have to divide the three given sides by 20. This means drawing a triangle with sides 10cm by 7.2cm by 6cm.

1 Construct this triangle (you will need to use compasses). Write the scale next to it.

Join the mid-point of the longest side to the opposite corner and measure this distance.

You should get 4.3 or 4.4cm for this.
Then using the scale again we convert back to metres by multiplying this by 20. This gives a final answer of 86 or 88m.

2 Write the scale 20m = 1cm in ratio form as shown at the end of Example 4.

3 Using a suitable scale make a careful plan of your classroom.

EXERCISE 2

Give your answers to the following to 2 significant figures.

a Find the length of the diagonal of a square of side 300m.

b The triangle ABC has a right angle at A, AB=70cm and BC=1m. The bisector of angle B meets the opposite side at X. Find BX.

c The diagram shows the end view of a bungalow. Find the total height.

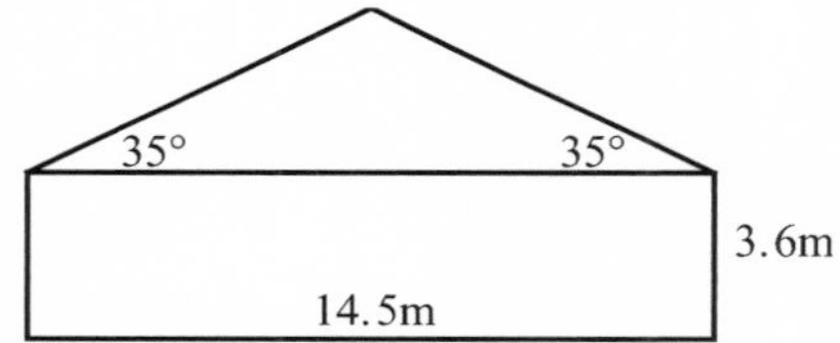

d Using a scale of 20:1 construct the rectangle WXYZ where WX=1.6m and XY=50cm.
Find the distance of the mid point of WZ from X.

e In the triangle PQR PQ=16mm, QR=30mm and PR=34mm. Draw an enlarged version of this triangle. The bisector of P meets the bisector of Q at S. Find SR.

f A man 6ft tall finds the angle between the horizontal direction and the direction of the top of a building to be 32°. If he is standing 120 feet from the base of the building find the height of the building (see diagram).

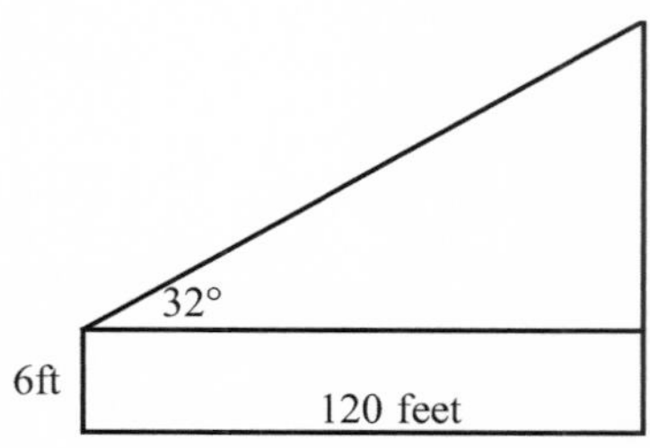

BEARINGS

You will be familiar with the directions of the compass: North, South, East and West.

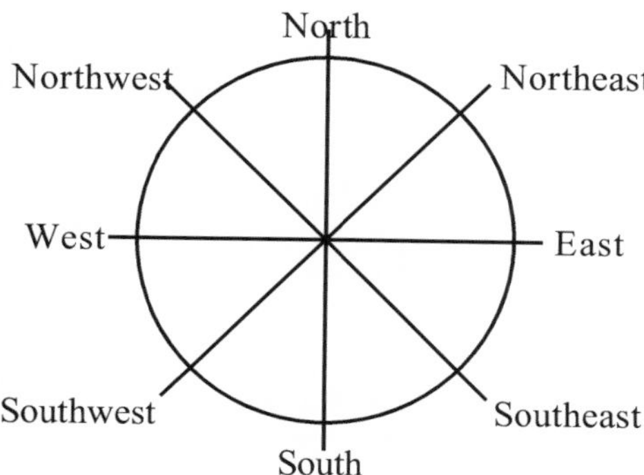

There are other directions as shown in the diagram above.
Northwest, for example, is exactly half way between the north and west directions.
This means there is an angle of 45° between each of these directions.

> A bearing is a direction or angle measured clockwise from the North direction.
> We always suppose the North direction to be vertically upwards on our page.

So, for example, if you travelled northeast this could be described by the bearing 045° (bearings are always given with 3 figures) because northeast is halfway between north and east.

And a bearing of 135° would be the same as a direction southeast.

EXERCISE 3

Convert the following directions to bearings (angles):

a east **b** south **c** southwest

d west **e** north **f** northwest

Convert the following bearings to compass directions: **g** 090° **h** 225° **i** 315°

USING BEARINGS

The position of a point, relative to some other point, can be described in various ways.
It could be described, for example, by a pair of coordinates: P(3,4) means go 3 units to the right from O and then 4 units up.

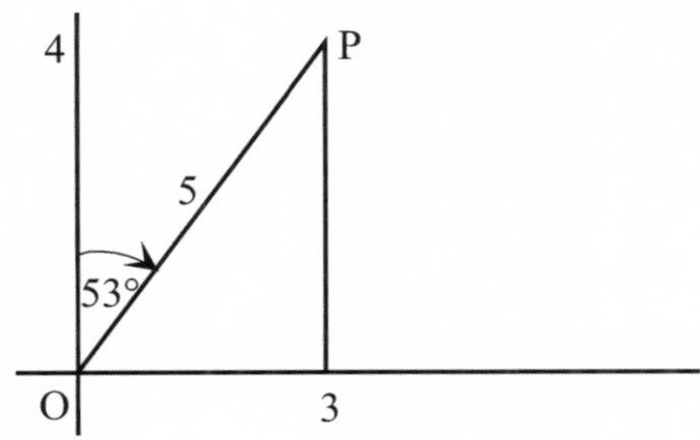

But this position could also be described by giving the bearing of P from O and its distance from O. We could say P has a bearing of 053° and is 5 units from O.

EXAMPLE 6

Show the position of point O,

a a point A which is on a bearing of 073° from a

b a point B on a bearing of 240° from a point O and
c a point C on a bearing of 340° froma point O.

a)

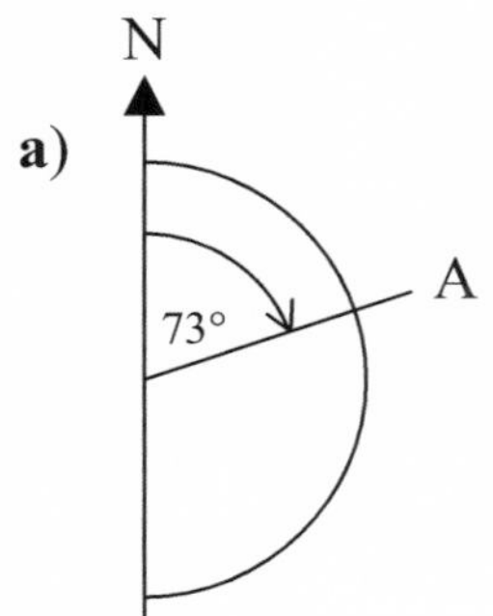

b)

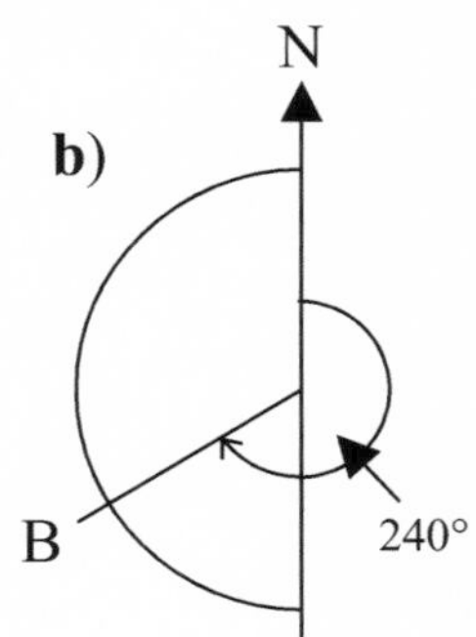

c)

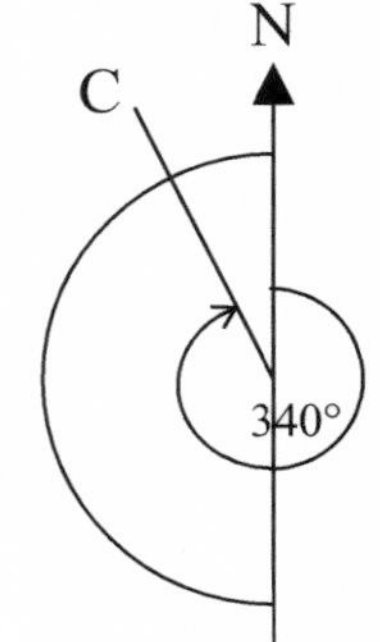

In each case begin by marking the point, O, in the middle of the page and drawing the north line in. ☞

a Place your protractor with the centre at O and the base line of the protractor along the north line. See the first diagram above.

Measure clockwise from the north to find 73° and make a mark there. Join this to O and write the angle as shown.

b If you have not got a circular protractor then for B and C you will have to lay the protractor on the other side, as shown.

Since 180° brings you round to the south direction you need another 60° to get 240°.
So measure 60° clockwise from the south and mark B.

c Similarly for C you can measure 160° from the south, or better still is to measure 20° backwards from the north because 340° is 20° short of the full 360°.

EXERCISE 4

Draw a diagram showing the following bearings:

a 30° **b** 145° **c** 200° **d** 260° **e** 310° **f** 95°

EXAMPLE 7

If the bearing of P from Q is 235° what is the bearing of Q from P?

It is not necessary to make an accurate drawing for this.
A sketch is sufficient.

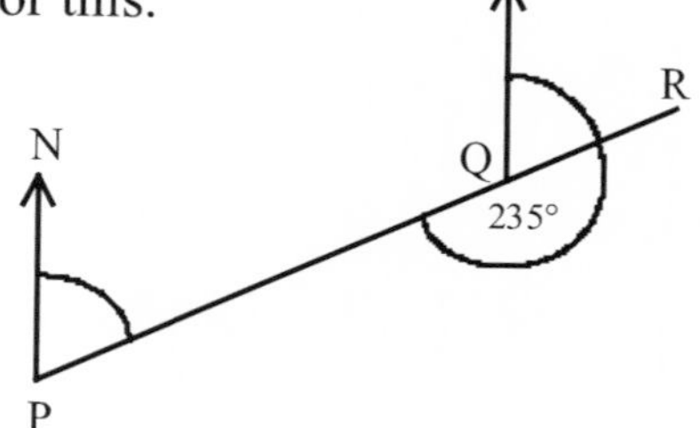

The sketch shows the positions of P and Q. By drawing a north line at P we can then see that the bearing of Q from P is the angle marked.

Next if we extend the line PQ to say R then we can see that angle NQR is the same as the required angle (they are F-angles). And we can see from the way the 235° has been split up that we can get the answer by taking 180° from 235° giving an answer of <u>55°</u>.

In the following questions draw two north lines each time and look for F and Z-angles.

EXERCISE 5

Find the bearing of Y from X given that the bearing of X from Y is

a 290° **b** 195° **c** 160° **d** 75° **e** 330° **f** 133°

Find the size of the angle marked x in each of the following sketches:

g

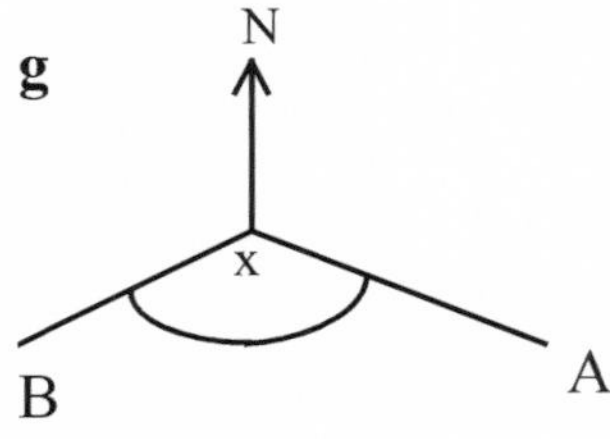

Bearing of A is 105°,
bearing of B is 230°.

h

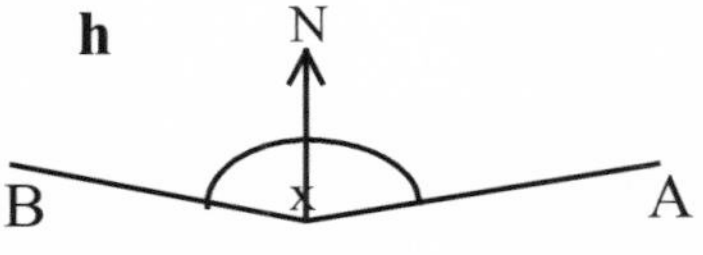

Bearing of A is 75°,
bearing of B is 290°.

i

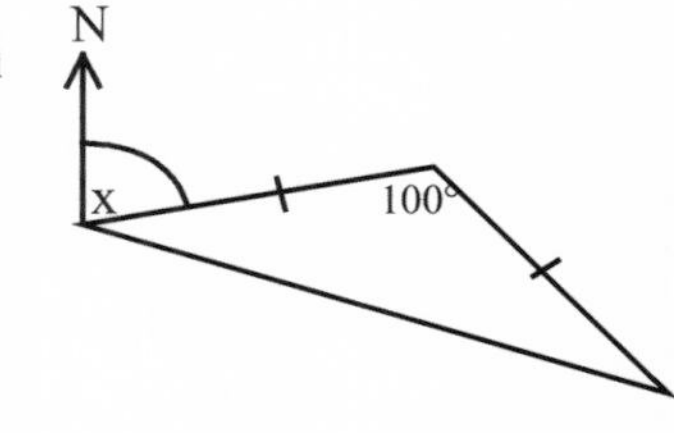

Bearing of A is 100°.

> To find the bearing of Y from X, given the bearing of X from Y, there is a simple rule we can use: If the angle is less than 180° we add 180°;
> and if the angle is greater than 180° we subtract 180°.

✵ Check your answers to **a** to **f** by this method.

EXAMPLE 8

A ship sails for 10 km on a bearing of 110° from a harbour H to a point X, and then sails for 7km on a bearing of 040° to a point Y.
By means of a scale drawing find the bearing of H from Y and the distance the ship must travel to return directly to the harbour.

☞

First we mark the harbour H, and then draw in a north line going upwards. Then using a protractor we can draw the 110° bearing as shown below.

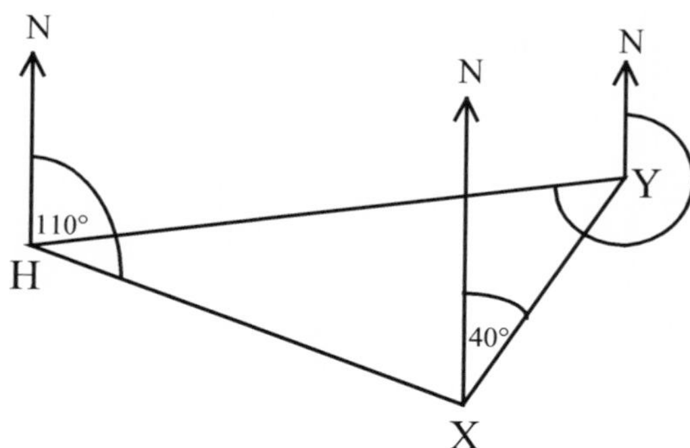

Next we must choose a suitable scale. Say 1cm = 2km. This means we measure 5cm along the line. This gives us the position of X.
Next we draw a north line at X and draw a bearing of 040°. According to our scale this line should be 3½cm long.

The bearing of H from Y is found by drawing in a north line at Y and measuring the angle shown. This should be 262°.

The distance required is HY, and by measurement this is 7.0cm, which according to our scale is 14.0km.

EXERCISE 6

a A ship A is due east of a lighthouse and 20km from it. Another ship B is 40km from the lighthouse and on a bearing of 051° from it. Using a scale of 1cm = 5km make a scale drawing and find the distance of B from A and the bearing of B from A.

b Three villages X, Y, Z have bearings of 020°, 130° and 230° from a point O respectively.
Their distances from O are 20km, 120km and 100km respectively.
Make an accurate scale drawing and find the distances XY, XZ and YZ.
Find also, by measurement, the bearing of Y from X, Z from Y and Z from X.

c A helicopter flies from base B on a bearing of 082° for 200km and then changes direction to fly on a bearing of 120° for 180km. By making an accurate drawing find his distance from B and the bearing he must take to return to base.

d ABC is an equilateral triangle with base AB=80m and B due east of A.
Find the bearing of C from A and the bearing of C from B.
Use a scale drawing to find the distance and bearing of the mid-point of BC from A.

RANGOLI PATTERNS

❋ On square spotty paper draw the following lines:

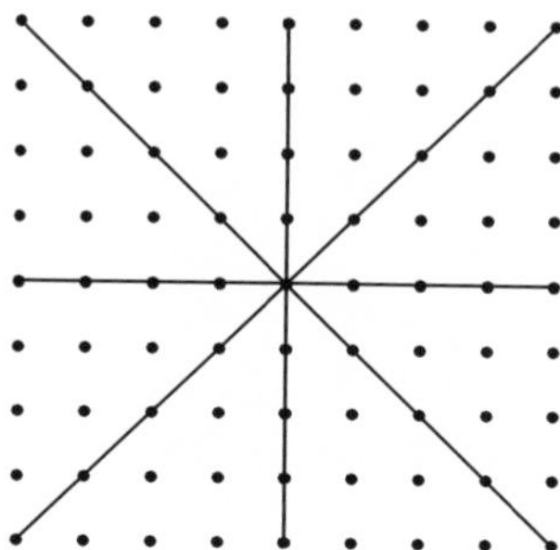

This is the base for a Rangoli pattern.
The four lines are four lines of symmetry.

We start with a line of our choice. Suppose we choose the one below:

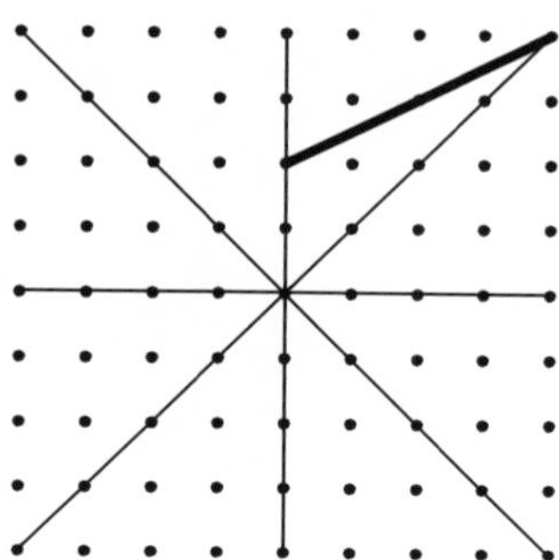

We then have to reflect the line in **all** the lines of symmetry.

First reflect the line in the vertical axis, then in the diagonal that goes from top left to bottom right, then in the horizontal axis and so on until after 7 reflections the following pattern is complete:

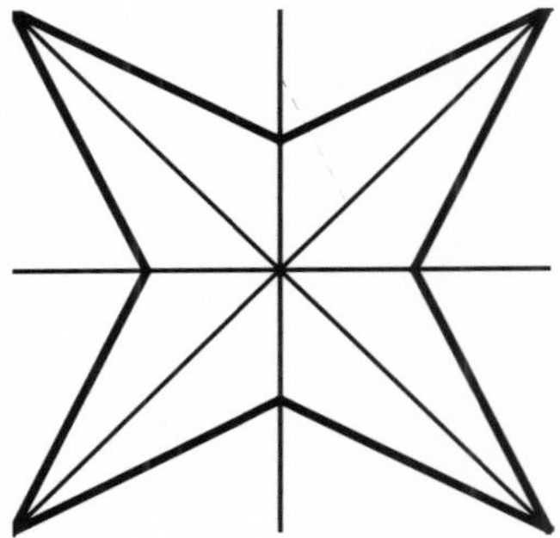

Now you can add another line and reflect it in all the axes of symmetry. For example the line shown dashed in the diagram above.

❋ Add the line shown to your diagram and reflect it in the lines of symmetry.

Now, since this figure fits in a square four of them will tessellate and so you could combine several of these together:

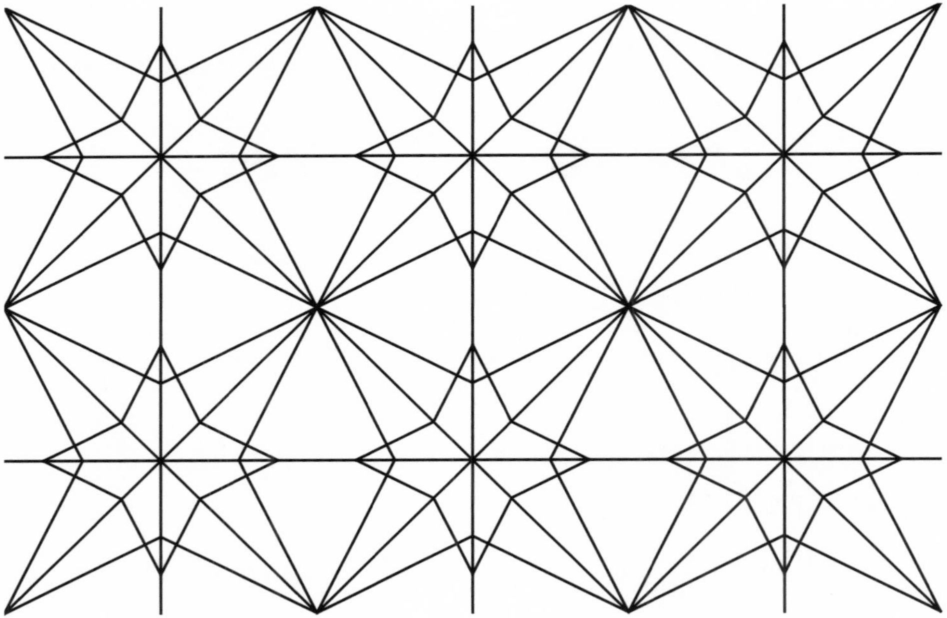

❋ Make a Rangoli pattern of your own, tessellate this pattern and colour it in.

Many Islamic designs are based on tessellated Rangoli patterns.

HISTORICAL NOTES

Bharati Krsna **Tirthaji** rediscovered Vedic Mathematics from ancient Vedic texts between 1911 and 1918. He wrote 16 books but only one is now available. He was a brilliant scholar and was appointed Shankaracharya (religious leader) in 1921. He sought world peace and unity between the East and the West.

Maharishi Mahesh Yogi is the founder of the world wide Transcendental Meditation movement and discoverer of the Absolute Number. He said that the Sutras of Vedic Mathematics are the software for the Cosmic Computer. The Cosmic Computer controls the behaviour of the universe on every scale and level.

Lewis **Carroll**, whose real name was Charles Dodgson, was a writer and lecturer at Oxford University. He wrote the famous children's classic *Alice in Wonderland* and other books.

Johannes **Kepler** was a German astronomer and court mathematician to Rudolph II of Prague. He is known for his three laws of planetary motion and sought inner relationships between the planets that would express the 'music of the spheres'.

Galileo Galilei was an astronomer and physicist who was one of the founding fathers of modern science. He made many important discoveries in applied mathematics. He was the first to point a telescope at the Sun, Moon and Stars but his findings were rejected by the Church.

Pierre Simon **Laplace** was a mathematician and physicist with a special interest in the motion of the planets and the moon. He also made many important mathematical discoveries.

Leopold **Kronecker** studied mathematics in Germany. His views on number were similar to those of the Pythagoreans. He argued against the theory of infinite sets which the mathematician Cantor developed at that time.

John D. **Barrow** is Professor of astronomy at the University of Sussex.

Plato is one of the most famous of the ancient Greek philosophers. He was a disciple of Socrates and founded an Academy at Athens. He believed that ideas are more real than the physical world and often used mathematics to illustrate his teachings.

St. Augustine was an early Christian theologian who lived a monastic life and wrote many books. The profound theology which he described dominated all later Western theology.

René **Descartes** was a philosopher and mathematician. He made a significant advance in mathematics which very simply combined the three branches of Arithmetic, Algebra and Geometry in Coordinate Geometry. In his philosophy he sought a system based on totally secure foundations for knowledge.

Sir James **Jeans** was an astronomer, physicist and mathematician who wrote primarily about cosmology. He was the first to propose the theory that matter is continuously created throughout the universe.

Sir Isaac **Newton** was a mathematician and physicist. He made enormous contributions in mathematics (including the discovery of the calculus), optics (including the reflecting telescope and breaking sunlight into colours), mechanics and astronomy (including his famous theory of universal gravitation) etc. He was a modest man who was also absorbed in theological studies.

Jules-Henri **Poincaré** was a mathematician and a philosopher of science. His most important work was in applying calculus to the prediction of planetary positions. Like Newton he was absent-minded and would think continuously for hours when developing his ideas.

Archimedes was a mathematician in ancient Greece. He made many important discoveries in geometry. He also invented many ingenious machines when the city in which he lived was under siege by the Romans: huge catapults, a machine for firing showers of missiles through a hole in the wall, machines with long adjustable poles for dropping large weights on the enemy ships and so on.

Proclus was a philosopher and mathematician in ancient Greece. He was a man of great energy and learning and wrote commentaries on earlier authors, particularly Plato.